FULL POTENTIAL

A Professional Development Guidebook
For Getting Clear On Your Career And Life Choices

"Personal fulfillment for me has been the freedom to chase my wildest dreams to the very ends of my ambitions. Through trial and error I eventually constructed a life that I can't wait to wake up to every morning. Nicole's *Full Potential* guide is the step-by-step framework I wish I'd had early on to avoid wasting even one second of time living outside of, or confused about, my purpose. There is simply no excuse not to afford yourself this level of clarity and road-mapping for a direct route to a more joyful, productive, and successful life."

Jaunique Sealey
Executive, Author, and Entrepreneur

"In career and life we need to balance making and letting things happen. This masterful workbook helps people at any stage of life with both. Life is best lived with action AND reflection. This collection of wisdom and exercises, composed by Nicole who is a talented life guide, supercharges both domains. It's a blueprint for fully BEing that you will empty a pen in."

Bryan Breckenridge
Founding Executive Director of box.org
Former Director of Nonprofits for Salesforce and LinkedIn
Founder of beliefenergy.com

"I was one of Nicole's first students and, let me tell you, she has a real gift for leading you through a self-reflective journey of career exploration. I learned so many important kernels of wisdom about myself, and I learned to be proud of the parts of myself I was once insecure about. Going through her program changed my life. I feel new and revitalized, and actually placed on the right path."

Lindsay Stanley
Former student of GROWmyfuture.org
Social Welfare Industry

"*Full Potential* is an absolute must-have for everyone. In order to be happy and truly fulfilled, we must engage in work that fulfill us from within; work that aligns with who we are at the core. I am excited and proud that Nicole has put this out into the world. It is a gift from the Universe. We need more people who come alive and are engaged in what they do every single day."

Mo Seetubtim
Founder of the Happiness Planner

Published in California, United States
Printed in the USA

ISBN - 9780578597584

Some readers may find it beneficial to further reflect on the insights gained, or may need further support. For more guidance and information visit:
www.vekitapd.com

Connect with us and others going through the same process on social media:
Facebook Groups: Vekita Full Potential - Insta: @vekitapd - LinkedIn: Vekita

On average high school counselors only have the capacity to spend five minutes to talk to students about what they want to do after high school. GROW solves this problem by training educators to deliver a curriculum, similar to Full Potential, that helps instill confidence, agency, and competencies in high school students empowering them to align who they are with career opportunities; so they remain engaged in school and life, stay away from crime, and become thriving, contributing members of society.

Please consider donating to: **GROWmyfuture.org**

VEKITA

PROFESSIONAL DEVELOPMENT

DEDICATED TO

Those who have encouraged and supported me to fulfill my potential. It is because of all of you that this guidebook will help so many others soar.

FULL POTENTIAL

Who am I? What is my purpose? What do I want to do with my life? Among all of life's big questions, these are the ones that I find the most important for living a fulfilled life, and the questions I have spent the last twenty years researching.

Not knowing what you want to do with your life, or whether you are on the right path, can be stressful. In my late teens and early twenties I used to regularly enter into mental loops of anxiety around the pressure of trying to figure out my career and life path. *What did I want to do with my life?* The decision seemed unbearably large. Stunted by anxiety around making the right choice, I would make no choice at all or go with what I thought I should do versus what was congruent and best for my well-being. I wondered, how do I make such a choice? A choice that would influence the rest of my life, AND one for which I had no guidance!

The questions loomed like a lingering grey cloud over my head, which made it hard to gain any kind of clarity. There is often a great deal of pressure, be it from our families, our colleagues, our culture, or most potently, from ourselves to choose a perfect career path. It occurred to me that I was not the only one experiencing the stress and anxiety of trying to find my life's path, and that there were not a lot of resources available to help guide people, like myself, through the process of understanding how one's talents can best fit into the workforce. There were many years I felt incredibly frustrated because I knew deep down within that I was not living my full potential. Waiting for clarity, regarding what I should do with my life, was like trying to get ready in the morning when the mirror is fogged up. You can see a blurry image, but you can't see clearly enough to do anything effectively. Through many years of self-exploration and education, I have gained a deeper understanding of my purpose. Part of my life's purpose is to help others also find their true north - and fulfill their full potential.

What do I want to do with my life? It is a question we all ponder at one point or another. For some, the answer comes easily. However, from what I have observed, that is rare. For most people it takes a series of life events to help them discover what to do. Some people, even after a lifetime, don't fully figure it out. It is easy to continue doing what is comfortable, familiar, and financially stable. It takes strength and courage to shake things up and choose a path that is more fulfilling. It is a choice. You get to choose what you want to focus on. Life is similar to a "Choose Your Own Adventure" book. No matter the path there will be benefits and challenges to where you focus your time and energy. There is no right or wrong in the choice you make; just different experiences.

Don't beat yourself up if you feel you have been headed in the wrong direction. This is normal. We learn from each experience - those deemed failures and those deemed successes. They are a part of who we are. There can be serendipity in life choices that didn't feel right in the moment, but end up being beneficial in the future in ways we couldn't even begin to imagine. For example, my frustration and winding path led me to write this guidebook. Another example is how Steve Jobs sat in on a calligraphy class, which eventually inspired the elegance that Apple is known for. "It was the first computer with beautiful typography," Jobs said. "If I had never dropped in on that single course in college, the Mac would have never had multiple typefaces or proportionally spaced fonts." Jobs also said, "You can only connect the dots looking backwards and not looking forward." Trust in your path. Everything we experience in life is useful.

Some people find one career they love and stick with it for life. Others may have multiple meaningful jobs. The key is to gain a deep understanding of your unique internal blueprint and the direction that is most congruent for you. Once you have identified the foundation of who you are, you can use this as a framework that can always be revisited and amended. In fact, it is important to reevaluate your life from time to time because circumstances and perspectives can shift.

Living in alignment with who you are will give you a greater sense of fulfillment and happiness, and can lead to greater economic success. It will not only impact you personally, but it will impact those around you as well — including friends, family, coworkers, and even strangers. According to an academic paper titled "The Psychology of Purpose," published by the John Templeton Foundation, being aligned with your purpose increases productivity and accomplishment as well as giving people a sense of meaning in their life, which leads to many personal health benefits.

As the architect of your life, you must first create a blueprint to follow. Most people have never had the tools or taken the time to develop their life's blueprint. Without a blueprint, you live your life by trial and error. That is how I lived most of my life, and in part it was a fun adventure. However, if I had the tools you are about to receive, it would have cut down on my stress and anxiety, and I would have been further along on my path.

By utilizing this guidebook, you will move out of wanting or dreaming about a certain life and into creating it for yourself, but you will have to work hard. It is a commitment you will need to make to yourself. With the help of this guidebook, you will explore yourself in a way most people never get the opportunity to do. Living your full potential means you will not only be living your best possible life, but you will also be living a life that will have a much greater impact on those around you and on society because you will be living fully and authentically, and bringing your greatest gifts out into the world!

As you go through this guidebook, know that there is no wrong answer, and that no decision has to be a permanent decision. Make this guidebook your own. The best approach is one without judgement or the need for perfection. Being a perfectionist myself, I have learned that sometimes I need to let go in order to have the answers come through me. Play with this guidebook. You can always make changes - and you might be positively surprised with some of your less managed or less refined answers.

It is my joy to help individuals, such as yourself, identify what careers are in alignment with your unique blueprint. I hope you enjoy the journey you are about to embark on; where you will discover all the multifaceted layers of what makes you who you are and the gifts you have to offer to the world.

Warmest regards,

Nicole Serena Silver

VEKITA
"awake" in the esperanto language:
to become conscious or aware of something

FULL
not lacking or omitting anything; complete

POTENTIAL
existing in possibility: capable of development into actuality

My main intention with this guidebook is to:

☐ Discover more about myself

☐ Advance within my current role

☐ Reevaluate or adjust my current career choices

☐ Make sure I am living my full potential

☐ Find a major/career

☐ Transition careers

☐ Establish short and long-term goals within my life

☐ Optimize living a happy and healthy life

☐ See what emerges

☐ Other

My commitment to myself is:

(Some suggestions: spend five hours a week working on *Full Potential*, finish this guidebook before the new year, put in the work needed to achieve the goals I identify for myself, etc.)

THE BREAKDOWN

Vision without action is a daydream. Action without vision is a nightmare.

- Japanese Proverb

This guidebook is an investment in yourself, the most important investment you can make. What you put into this guidebook is what you will get out of it. Some of the activities take brain power. That is why the guidebook is broken down into weekly segments so the content does not feel overwhelming. However, please feel free to go through the content at whatever pace you like. Going through this guidebook with a group or friend is a great experience and motivator, but can also be done successfully independently.

Full Potential is an introspective process that requires concentrated time. Scheduling time on your calendar is suggested.

"If you don't make the time to work on creating the life you want, you are eventually going to be forced to spend a lot of time dealing with a life you don't want.

- Kevin Ngo

NATURE AND NURTURE
Suggested Weekly Activities

WHO YOU ARE
Suggested Weekly Activities

WHAT DO YOU WANT IN YOUR LIFE
Suggested Weekly Activities

ALIGNING WHO YOU ARE WITH YOUR CAREER
Suggested Weekly Activities

TOOLS FOR SUCCESS
At Your Own Pace

TIPS FOR DIFFERENT LIFE STAGES
Find Your Section

FULL POTENTIAL

* Weekly suggested activities typically take 1-1.5 hours. You may want to divide the time into two 45 minute sittings. Work-Life Integration and (In)formational Interviews will take longer.

NATURE & NURTURE
FROM BIRTH TO PRESENT DAY
YOUR HISTORY AND HOW IT HAS SHAPED YOU

Sometimes thinking about the future requires reflecting on the past. Knowing your past patterns helps you build towards your ideal future. Your past does not define you; it prepares you for whatever is next.

- Nicole Serena Silver

NATURE

"The two most important days in your life are the day you were born and the day you find out why.

- Mark Twain

YOUR INNATE QUALITIES

We all come into this world with our unique blueprint. Babies are born with personalities and tendencies. For example as a baby I was very calm, even during my mom's pregnancy -- that's why I was given the middle name of Serena. In my adult years people have commented on how peaceful and calm I am. Another example is when I was a baby, my parents would take me with them to gatherings. While other babies were sleeping, I would be awake wanting to witness everything. Fast forward 30+ years and not a lot has changed. I love exploring and don't want to miss out on anything this world has to offer.

Who knew you as a baby (ideally age zero-three)? Schedule a conversation to ask what kind of qualities you had when you were young. This can be an engaging and meaningful conversation for both you and the person you speak with. Write the notes from your conversation on the next page. Here are some sample questions you can ask:

- What was I like as a baby and toddler?

- What was my temperament?

- What was my personality?

- How did I interact with adults or other children?

- Did I take interest in any specific types of activities?

- What kinds of things got me excited?

- What was it like caring for me?

- What was my sleep pattern?

- Are there any moments that stand out to you from when I was a baby or toddler?

FULL POTENTIAL

Notes about what kind of baby and/or toddler you were:

_____

_____

_____

_____

_____

_____

_____

_____

_____

_____

_____

_____

_____

_____

_____

_____

What are the qualities you had as a baby or toddler that have stayed consistent over time?

What childhood traits appear within work or school?

What childhood traits appear within your personal life?

FULL POTENTIAL

NURTURE

Your past forms you, whether you like it or not. Each encounter and experience has its own effect, and you're shaped the way the wind shapes a mesquite tree on a plain.

- Lance Armstrong

LIFE MAP

There are many complex aspects that contribute to a person's makeup. Your life journey influences your perspective, responses, actions, and how your life has been shaped. Let's take a look at your history of what has helped make you into the person you are today.

Identify key moments in your life that were significant and helped shape you into who you are today. A good way to review your life story is to start with when you were born and move through to the present in five-year intervals. You can brainstorm and draft your life map on a blank piece of paper before adding the completed version into the guidebook. You may find that there were back-to-back years that had significant impact, and chunks of time where no influential events occurred. All of our lives look different. Design your historic map to best represent your life story.

Stanley Martin Lieber aka
STAN LEE
LIFE MAP EXAMPLE

[2017]
Wife Joan dies
I will see you in the afterlife

[1988]
**First appearance
in a movie**
More than Hitchcock

[1961]
**The Fantastic
was created**
Excelsior!

[1968]
Stan's Soapbox
Let's lay it right on the line

[1962]
Amazing Fantasy #15
My spidey senses are tingling

[1953]
Daughter Jan is born
A life taken too soon

[1942]
**United States Army
Signal Corps**
My own variation of
Captain America

[1950]
**Daughter
J.C. is born**
It's all love

[1941]
**Began working in
comics & met
Jack Kirby**
Nuff said

[1947]
**Married Jan Clayton
Boocock**
Sketched before I knew you &
now drawn in my heart

[1937]
**Biggest News of the
Week Contest**
Winning changed my life

[1929]
The Great Depression
One bedroom, parents sleeping
on foldout couch

[1931]
Brother Larry Born
Lieber legacy x2

[1922]
Stan Lee Born
In the beginning...

YOUR LIFE MAP

Label each monumental event with: **1)** A title representing the experience and **2)** The impact it had on you.

REFLECTION

What significant moments stood out to you? And why?

Can you identify any patterns with how you approached multiple significant events? Such as disposition, skills, mindset, emotions, etc.

How has the past shaped who you are today?

PEOPLE WHO HAVE IMPACTED YOU

Who are the people that had the biggest influence on your life (good and bad) and what are the main qualities they embedded in you?

👤 NAME:

INFLUENCE:

👤 NAME:

INFLUENCE:

👤 NAME:

INFLUENCE:

👤 NAME:

INFLUENCE:

FULL POTENTIAL

WHO YOU ARE

Knowing yourself is the beginning of all wisdom.

- Aristotle

INTROSPECTION

The Japanese believe in a concept called Ikigai, which is defined as your reason for being or purpose in life. Ikigai is composed of two words; iki (life) and kai (realization of hopes and dreams). According to the Japanese, every single person has Ikigai.

The introspection chapter will help you become self aware of all the parts that make you who you uniquely are. This is essential for moving into your full potential. Each section will illuminate different parts of yourself; which you will then turn into a cohesive road map for your professional development.

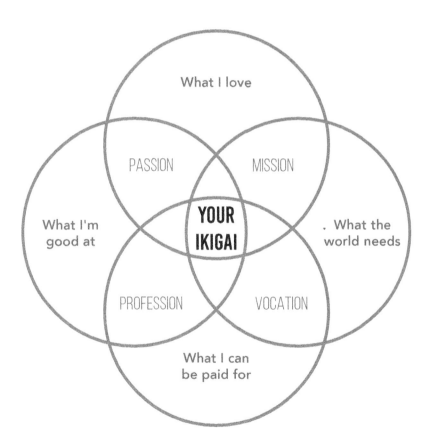

PASSION

Working hard for something we don't care about is called stress. Working hard for something we love is called passion.

- Simon Sinek

PERSPECTIVES ON PASSION

"Find your passion" or "follow your passion" echoes throughout society in an array of forms: advertising, inspirational websites, printed on merchandise, advice given from people wanting the best for us, etc. The sentiment of finding your passion is ultimately find a line of work that is fulfilling. Passion is just one piece of the equation of having a fulfilling career, but an important one to explore.

A common belief is to pursue interests only after passion has been found. Psychologists at Stanford decided to explore this concept. Through a series of studies they found that most people find their passion after trying something, discover they like it and become good at it! For example, I wanted to try salsa dancing, I tried it and enjoyed it, and then I took lessons to get good at it and now I have developed a passion for salsa dancing.

Other things to consider:
- Passion is energizing and helps drive success with your career.
- Passion in your career can take many forms, such as: being passionate about the people you are working with, the task you are doing, the experiences you are having, new learnings you are gaining, etc. Some passions do not belong in the workplace and may be better suited as something you do in your personal time.
- Passion has cycles of ups and downs with your degree of engagement. I love the analogy of passion being related to being with a life partner. The relationship will have ups and downs, but even when things aren't going well you still want to stay together with that person. Same with passion.
- Passions can change over time.

EXPERIMENT WITH DISCOVERING PASSION

- Reflect on times in your life when you felt energized and engaged. You can also keep a daily log to identify in the current moment how different activities make you feel. This will help you pinpoint activities that you enjoy doing.
- Take time to try new things. Remember, experimenting can lead to the discovery of passion. You can flip through the pages of magazines or go exploring in your city or town while asking yourself, "What would I like to explore more or what activities can I fall in love with?"

FULL POTENTIAL

UNLOCKING YOUR PASSION

I get joy from talking about:

....

Something I could do for eight hours and not get tired of is:

....

If I didn't have to go to school or work for a week, I'd spend the time:

....

I am the happiest when I am:

....

When I was a kid I wanted to become:

....

I use my creativity to:

....

I have always wanted to learn more about or experience:

....

Most people don't know that I really enjoy:

....

I am the first person my friends call when they need help with:

....

I have gotten compliments about my ability to:

....

Time goes by fast when I am:

....

Please rank your answers from most passionate (1) to least passionate (11).
If you get stuck, think about a life in which one activity plays a major role
and the other doesn't exist.

TOP THREE:

....

VEKITA

PASSION VISUALIZATION

Discovering your passions usually isn't uncovered through assessments. It has to come from within you. That is why this visualization was developed. Please set aside twenty undisturbed minutes in a quiet space and have a pencil and/or colored pens available for use after the visualization.

STEP 1 - Visit **vekitapd.com/resources** for the visualization.

STEP 2 - After you have listened to the visualization please take at least ten minutes to journal, draw, or express in any form you'd like about what came up for you during the visualization.

FULL POTENTIAL

SKILLS

Hard skills can land you jobs. Soft skills can make or break your career.

- Nicole Serena Silver

HARD SKILLS

Hard skills are specific knowledge and abilities that are typically more technical. For example: computer programming, graphic design, writing and editing, math, marketing, cooking, construction, research, etc.

Brainstorm: What are your hard skills?

....

....

....

....

SOFT SKILLS

Soft skills are non-technical skills, typically described as people skills or personal attributes. For example: communication, work ethic, adaptability, creative thinking, problem-solving, decision making, networking, etc.

Brainstorm: What are your soft skills?

....

....

....

....

Now for both the hard and soft skills, <u>underline</u> the skill you enjoy doing the most and ⟨circle⟩ the skill you are the best at.

FULL POTENTIAL

SKILLS MATRIX

A Gallup analysis titled, *Employees Who Use Their Strengths Outperform Those Who Don't*,[2] revealed that people who use their strengths every day are three times more likely to report having an excellent quality of life, six times more likely to be engaged at work, 8% more productive and 15% less likely to quit their jobs. Knowing what skills you have in your current inventory is essential and, of course, you can continuously add skills to your tool kit. In this activity you will examine prior accomplishments to better understand your current skill set.

What three accomplishments are you the most proud of?
(accomplishments can be anything -- work/school accomplishments, helping a family member overcome a problem, participating in a race, etc.)

1...

2...

3...

SKILLS MATRIX INSTRUCTIONS

1. You will be making a matrix for each of your three accomplishments. For each matrix, in the top grey column, write a brief description or label for one of your top accomplishments, such as starting a business.

2. For each accomplishment ask yourself, "What particular knowledge, skill, or ability did I have that contributed to my success with this particular accomplishment?" Write your answers to the question in the grey column to the left for all applicable skills, such as communication, problem solving, etc.

3. Next, highlight the specifics of how you used your skills on the right side of the matrix. For example, under communication you could write "presenting to funders." You may find that you create a matrix with some squares that have robust information and others with less. Even though some squares may be more robust in content, squares that have less content may have been more important to accomplishing the task or taken more time than the others.

WARNING: If you find yourself listing personality traits or characteristics, dig deeper into how that translates into skills. For example, instead of saying "I am easy going" break this down a bit further to describe what this means in the context of your past accomplishments. It might be better to state that you "work well under pressure" or that you are "adaptable to different work environments." You need to be listing your knowledge, skills, and abilities, not describing your personality.

EXAMPLE

	STARTING A BUSINESS		
Communication	Outreach to schools and teachers	Presenting to funders	Developing trainings
Problem Solving	Finding solvable ways to scale curriculum	Motivating unresponsive volunteers	Solving funding gaps
Creativity	Curriculum development	Marketing campaigns	Beautifying PowerPoints
Analytics	Measuring program impact		
Management	Overseeing a team of 20	Created and executed a strategy plan	
Other	Leadership and determination to see the organization succeed		

ACCOMPLISHMENT #1

ACCOMPLISHMENT #2

ACCOMPLISHMENT #3

MATRIX REVIEW

Is there overlap with the skills you used in all three accomplishments?

_____

_____

_____

_____

_____

_____

What stood out to you when looking at your skills?

_____

_____

_____

_____

_____

_____

_____

_____

_____

FULL POTENTIAL

Looking at both your brainstorming of hard and soft skills and the skills matrix, what are the top skills you are good at and enjoy doing?

Common Themes

Now that you have explored your passions and skills, what are some of your common themes?

Examples: you like structure, caring for people, innovative thinking or creative expression.

HOW PASSION AND SKILLS WORK TOGETHER

When love and skill work together, expect a masterpiece.

- John Ruskin

The quadrant below demonstrates how you want to be in a high-skills, high-passion area and what you can do to get to the intersection of high-skills and high-passion.

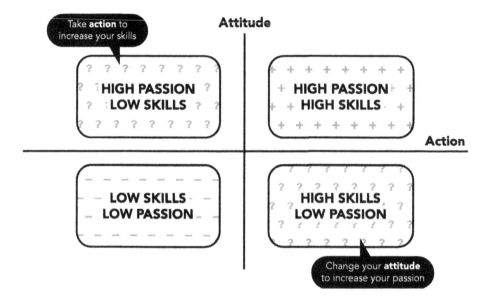

The rectangle with the minus signs represent "don't do it" - which is **LOW** skills and **LOW** passion.

The rectangle with the question marks represent a "maybe" - if you have **LOW** passion, but **HIGH** skills, you can potentially increase your passion by taking conscious action to change your attitude towards a job. If you are in the quadrant where you have **LOW** skills, but **HIGH** passion, you can take action and work on building your skills.

The rectangle with the plus signs represent "go for it" - this is **HIGH** passion and **HIGH** skill set. This means this is a job worth looking to pursue, because you are more likely to enjoy and stick with that career.

The main point is that you should try to avoid the area where you're not good at something and don't really enjoy it! Life is too short for that. However, you may be able to identify areas you are not good at YET, but interested in learning about and getting good at.

VEKITA

JOBS RELATED TO SKILLS AND PASSION

List your top five to ten skills and passions in the grid below. Next, discover job categories by experimenting with different combinations of how skills and passions overlap.

Do not feel that you need to identify a specific job title with this activity. Just think about overarching themes. For example, if a strong skill for you is organizing and one of your passions is music, a possible job could be to do production work in the music industry. Later you can explore titles that are related through online research, such as: tour manager, tour coordinator, production manager, festival director, etc. As you can see there are many kinds of jobs that could fit into the overarching category. If you want to start your online research now you are welcome to, and we will be dedicating time later in this guidebook specifically for that.

SKILLS	PASSIONS	JOB CATEGORIES

VALUES

When your values are clear, making decisions becomes easier.

- Roy E. Disney

PERSONAL AND PROFESSIONAL VALUES

Values act as a compass, guiding your beliefs, choices, and behaviors. They influence everything you do, but usually it happens unconsciously. In this section you will explore both your personal and professional values. You may find that there is overlap, and you may find there are diffenations. A differentiation could be that you value freedom in your personal life and structure in your job. Even if there is differentiation the both will still impact one another. If you value freedom in your personal life, it might be important to have a job that won't need you to work beyond your scheduled hours.

THE IMPORTANCE OF VALUES

- Awareness of your values leads to direction in your life and career.
- Values are expressions of what is important and meaningful to you.
- Values are standards that guide your decision making.
- If you don't live your values, it's harder to find fulfillment because you set yourself up for internal conflict, which leads to unhappiness. For example, a misalignment could be that you want to become an entrepreneur (which can be unstable), but you value safety and security. If your values are not aligned it can cause minor or even major issues.
- Knowing and understanding your values is critical for creating the life you want. This allows you to make more congruent choices, providing better results within your life. When your behavior matches your values, your fulfillment, satisfaction, and happiness often improve.
- Following your values will most likely lead to functioning at a higher capacity and greater prosperity.

PERSONAL VALUES

What values are important in your personal life? Below is a list of sample values. Check off any boxes you feel strongly about and add your own if they are not listed.

☐ Acceptance	☐ Dependability	☐ Imagination	☐ Resourcefulness
☐ Accomplishment	☐ Determination	☐ Independence	☐ Respect
☐ Accountability	☐ Dignity	☐ Innovation	☐ Sacrifice
☐ Adventure	☐ Directness	☐ Inquisitiveness	☐ Security
☐ Ambition	☐ Discipline	☐ Integrity	☐ Sensitivity
☐ Appreciation	☐ Diversity	☐ Intelligence	☐ Simplicity
☐ Assertiveness	☐ Dynamism	☐ Justice	☐ Spirituality
☐ Attentiveness	☐ Education	☐ Kindness	☐ Spontaneity
☐ Authenticity	☐ Efficiency	☐ Knowledge	☐ Stability
☐ Awareness	☐ Empathy	☐ Learning	☐ Success
☐ Balance	☐ Excellence	☐ Love	☐ Support
☐ Beauty	☐ Experience	☐ Maturity	☐ Thoroughness
☐ Boldness	☐ Exploration	☐ Mindfulness	☐ Thoughtfulness
☐ Calmness	☐ Expressiveness	☐ Open-mindedness	☐ Trust
☐ Candor	☐ Fairness	☐ Optimism	☐ Truth
☐ Change	☐ Faith	☐ Order	☐ Understanding
☐ Charity	☐ Family	☐ Originality	☐ Uniqueness
☐ Clarity	☐ Fitness	☐ Passion	☐ Variety
☐ Cleanliness	☐ Flexibility	☐ Patience	☐ Vision
☐ Cleverness	☐ Freedom	☐ Peace	☐ Wisdom
☐ Collaboration	☐ Friendship	☐ Perseverance	☐ Wonder
☐ Compassion	☐ Fun	☐ Playfulness	
☐ Confidence	☐ Generosity	☐ Pleasure	Other:
☐ Consistency	☐ Gratitude	☐ Power	
☐ Courage	☐ Growth	☐ Preparedness	....
☐ Courtesy	☐ Happiness	☐ Privacy	
☐ Creativity	☐ Harmony	☐ Punctuality	....
☐ Curiosity	☐ Health	☐ Purposefulness	
☐ Decisiveness	☐ Humility	☐ Reflection	....
☐ Dedication	☐ Humor	☐ Resilience	....

What are your top three personal values?

....

PROFESSIONAL VALUES

Check off values that are the most important to you within EACH category. Feel free to write in your own values if you think of one that is not listed.

ENVIRONMENT

- ☐ Collaborative workspace
- ☐ Private office
- ☐ Work remotely
- ☐ Work at specific location
- ☐ Set your own schedule
- ☐ Operate under planned deadlines
- ☐ Outdoors
- ☐ Aesthetically pleasing
- ☐ Fast-pace
- ☐ Casual and laid-back
- ☐ Social & fun
- ☐ Quiet
- ☐ Structured
- ☐ Unstructured
- ☐ Creative
- ☐ Professional
- ☐ Supportive
- ☐ Inclusive
- ☐ Family-Oriented
- ☐ Calm
- ☐ Public Interactions
- ☐ Other:

CONTENT

- ☐ Artistic/creative expression
- ☐ Problem solving
- ☐ Helping others
- ☐ Intellectually stimulating
- ☐ Teaching/ mentoring
- ☐ Learning
- ☐ Change & variety
- ☐ Stable & predictable
- ☐ Challenging
- ☐ Interacting with nature
- ☐ Interacting with people
- ☐ Interacting with animals
- ☐ Interacting with technology
- ☐ Building things
- ☐ Work that is adventurous
- ☐ Autonomous
- ☐ Take on multiple roles
- ☐ Highly skilled role
- ☐ Other:

RELATIONSHIPS

- ☐ Mutual respect
- ☐ Leading teams
- ☐ Open communication
- ☐ Trust
- ☐ Friendly competitiveness
- ☐ Collaborative
- ☐ Social interactions
- ☐ Formal relationships
- ☐ Supportive
- ☐ Individual projects
- ☐ Team collaboration
- ☐ Co-workers provide intellectual challenge
- ☐ Mentorship from senior staff
- ☐ Direct & honest
- ☐ Kindness
- ☐ Acknowledgment from co-workers
- ☐ Accepting & inclusivity
- ☐ Other:

PERSONAL

- ☐ Job security
- ☐ Leadership & Influence
- ☐ Making a difference
- ☐ Good work benefits
- ☐ Hands-on work
- ☐ Physically engaging
- ☐ Work that is adventurous
- ☐ Creativity & self-expression
- ☐ Independence
- ☐ Feeling comfortable
- ☐ Utilizing your expertise
- ☐ Respectable job title
- ☐ Work recognition
- ☐ Supportive management
- ☐ Belonging & sense of community
- ☐ Work-life balance
- ☐ Other:

Out of all the values you've selected pick your top three (3) most important. It is okay to pick values that are all in the same category if that is what matters the most to you!

Top Three

RELATIONSHIP TO YOUR VALUES

Reflecting on your personal and professional values, what three values do you spend the most time fulfilling? Choose three significant values to focus on for this activity. Use a different colored pen for each value and fill in your answers below. Feel free to do this with your other values on a blank piece of paper.

1 _____ 2 _____ 3 _____

MOTIVATION

Why is it important for you to apply your top three values? Example: Collaboration provides more well-rounded perspectives and sharing ideas gives me more inspiration and energy.

Value 1: _____

_____

Value 2: _____

_____

Value 3: _____

_____

ORIGIN

Where did each of your values come from? Who instilled them in you? For example, parent or guardian, other family, friends, teachers, community leaders, religion, culture, media (TV, news, books, etc.) or something else.

Value 1: _____

Value 2: _____

Value 3: _____

SHOULD (external -- others' values) vs. WANT (internal -- your values)

- Focusing on what you "should" do is not sustainable or healthy.
- Focusing on what you "want" to do motivates you in the long term because you're acting in congruence with what matters to you.

Are your values stemming from a place of "should" or "want" or a combination of both?

☐ ☐ ☐ Should   ☐ ☐ ☐ Want   ☐ ☐ ☐ Both should and want

VEKITA _____

VALUES EVALUATION

Now that you have examined how your values are influenced, how do you feel about them? Do you want to modify or revise any of your top values? Do you feel more strongly aligned with them?

How do your values currently influence your life?

When have you diverted away from your values and why?

What are ways you can apply your values more in your life?

FULL POTENTIAL

PERSONALITY

Diversity of perspectives challenges us to see the world in different ways; promoting depth, wisdom, expansive thinking, growth, and balance. Some of the most powerful tools are knowing oneself, recognizing other perspectives, and understanding how different personalities interact.

- Nicole Serena Silver

PERSONALITY TYPES

Understanding your personality is a powerful tool. So powerful, that countless variations of personality tests have been developed. I have explored a lot of them, Myers Briggs, DiSC, Color Code, etc. All are good. I prefer to work with the Enneagram because it has a more holistic and all-encompassing approach. There are many layers to uncover with personalities and the Enneagram digs deep into the intricacy of human patterns. Understanding your personality can help you gain insight into things such as your communication style, how you act when you are under pressure versus when you are relaxed, your likes and dislikes, and so on. Additionally, it can be extremely helpful with understanding others and how to best work with their strengths and weaknesses.

Just as with leadership styles, we incorporate all the qualities of each personality type. There are thousands of variations in which we can express ourselves and none of us fit into a single personality type exactly. However, we all have our knee-jerk reaction to situations and an inherent pattern we gravitate towards more that is related to a specific personality type.

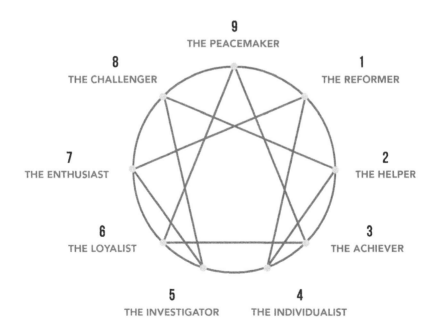

PERSONALITY TYPES
BASED ON THE ENNEAGRAM

What is your predominant personality type?
Mark the boxes that you strongly relate to

 Type 1

Are you a rule-following person who notices small details?　☐ YES ☐ NO

Highlights	Struggles
☐ I have strong ethics.	☐ My attention goes towards errors and I can be critical of others.
☐ I am a hard worker and deliver quality results.	☐ Small imperfections bother me.
☐ When relaxed, I am spontaneous and wise.	☐ When stressed, I am moody and irrational.

Type 2

Are you a people-person who wants to make sure everyone is happy? ☐ YES ☐ NO

Highlights	Struggles
☐ I am empathetic to the feelings and needs of others.	☐ I get emotionally hurt easily.
☐ I make friends easily and relate to people.	☐ I constantly seek approval and need others to like me.
☐ When relaxed, I am altruistic and love unconditionally.	☐ When stressed, I am more overbearing and possessive.

Type 3

Are you a success-oriented person who inspires others?　☐ YES ☐ NO

Highlights	Struggles
☐ People may think of me as confident and/or charming.	☐ One of the worst possible things is to look dumb.
☐ I am ambitious and competent with accomplishing tasks.	☐ I am a workaholic.
☐ When relaxed, I am more capable and dependable.	☐ When stressed, I can become deceptive so my mistakes aren't exposed.

Type 4

Are you a creative person who deeply experiences emotions?　☐ YES ☐ NO

Highlights	Struggles
☐ I am introspective and experience feelings in a deep and intense way. ☐ I am thoughtful with things like how I dress and gifts I give. ☐ When relaxed, I am profoundly creative and self-aware.	☐ I can be dramatic and unload my emotions onto others. ☐ I can't stand the ordinary and experience envy ☐ When stressed, I feel hopeless and emotionally paralyzed.

Type 5

Are you a curious person who likes to have everything figured out?　☐ YES ☐ NO

Highlights	Struggles
☐ I am curious and seek knowledge. ☐ I am independent, innovative, and inventive. ☐ When relaxed, I am more analytical and insightful.	☐ I feel insecure in a crowd and lack people skills. ☐ I can become detached from feelings. ☐ When stressed, I am more isolated and intense.

Type 6

Are you a security oriented person who can link many ideas together? ☐ YES ☐ NO

Highlights	Struggles
☐ I am reliable, loyal, and value truth. ☐ I am good at finding gaps in systems and tracking situations around me. ☐ When relaxed, I am more carefree and optimistic.	☐ I tend to imagine the worst-case scenario is happening. ☐ I can become reactive and volatile. ☐ When stressed, I am more anxious and defensive.

FULL POTENTIAL

Type 7

Are you a spontaneous person who is always seeking new experiences? ☐YES ☐NO

Highlights	Struggles
☐ I am a visionary with a vivid imagination.	☐ I can be undisciplined and get distracted.
☐ I seek fun and can find joy in almost anything.	☐ I might abandon things when they are no longer fun or interesting.
☐ When relaxed, I am more playful and fascinated by life.	☐ When stressed, I am more scattered and impatient.

Type 8

Are you an assertive person who can easily step in to take charge? ☐ YES ☐ NO

Highlights	Struggles
☐ I fight for justice and protect the weak.	☐ I can be pushy and controlling.
☐ I am straightforward and decisive.	☐ I don't always consider the feelings of others.
☐ When relaxed, I am more resourceful and caring.	☐ When stressed, I am more fearful and aggressive.

Type 9

Are you a stable person who tries to create harmony around you? ☐ YES ☐ NO

Highlights	Struggles
☐ I am accepting of others and am easy to be around.	☐ I avoid conflict and saying "no" to people.
☐ I keep a routine, but will go with the flow.	☐ I don't like making decisions and hide from problems.
☐ When relaxed, I am more energetic and engage in my personal development.	☐ When stressed, I am more numb and self-sacrificing.

? What personality type do you most relate to the most?

LEADERSHIP

Each and every one of us are leaders. You are a leader with every action and word. Your choices and actions impact you and everyone around you, whether you are conscious of it or not.

- Nicole Serena Silver

LEADERSHIP

Each and every one of us are leaders. What leadership style are you? Mark the boxes that you strongly relate to.

LEADERSHIP STYLE L

Enjoys using words like options, potential, and imagine

- ☐ Visionary; looks ahead and focuses on where they want to be
- ☐ Thinks strategically and sees the big picture; understands how all the parts and people need to work together
- ☐ Looks for and easily sees patterns or similarities
- ☐ Likes to have a lot of information when making decisions
- ☐ Pushes for growth (their own and others')
- ☐ Enjoys problem solving, and is good at it
- ☐ Likes to experiment with new ideas
- ☐ Likes to take the lead on exploration
- ☐ Enjoys a creative challenge
- ☐ Enjoys coming up with many possible solutions to a challenge
- ☐ Works outside the box; comes up with new and creative ways to do things
- ☐ Quick to see valuable opportunities and jumps at them

LEADERSHIP STYLE E

Enjoys using words like fair, right, and cooperation

- ☐ Works well with others to better understand a situation
- ☐ Likes to hear other people's thoughts and ideas in order to make decisions
- ☐ Understands the different ways people need to take in information, so they can take action on it
- ☐ Good listening skills; especially notices feelings and emotions
- ☐ Encourages others to contribute
- ☐ Doesn't enjoy the feeling of competition
- ☐ Usually focuses on what is happening in the current moment
- ☐ Uses relationships and interactions to get things done
- ☐ Has a strong sense of how people should be treated
- ☐ Gives people the benefit of the doubt; trusts people unless they break that trust
- ☐ Prefers to believe others' statements at face value
- ☐ Trusts their gut/instinct/intuition; their intuition feels like truth, and they trust it

LEADERSHIP STYLE Ⓐ

Values words like analyze, data, and verify

- ☐ Understands what information is needed when making decisions; practical and thorough in decision-making
- ☐ Is careful to make sure to use proper instructions, guidelines, and clear ways of getting things done
- ☐ Uses information and logic to make decisions
- ☐ Weighs all sides of an issue
- ☐ Good at managing day-to-day details
- ☐ Tends to think about and analyze the actions they take
- ☐ Maximizes existing resources
- ☐ Looks at how to reuse ways of doing things from the past rather than starting from scratch
- ☐ Doesn't waste resources and understands the limitations of the situation
- ☐ Organized and likes to do things the same way each time unless there's a good reason to change
- ☐ Enjoys planning and adding resources to the team
- ☐ Trusts logic and facts over feelings

LEADERSHIP STYLE Ⓓ

Values words like execution, accountability, and action

- ☐ Is strong minded; is willing to push for what they want
- ☐ Thinks in terms of final needs/goals
- ☐ Takes charge and cares about performance
- ☐ Has high standards for self and others
- ☐ Enjoys challenges from difficult situations and people
- ☐ Likes doing many types of tasks, and things that are new
- ☐ Doesn't get upset with being told no, but wants to understand why
- ☐ Easily takes on decision-making role and is good at giving direction
- ☐ Is comfortable stepping in when problems arise
- ☐ Makes decisions easily and with confidence
- ☐ Quick to decide and act; likes others to take action quickly
- ☐ Comfortable with unknown territory

Tally up your answers for each section. It is common to end up with styles that are in equal ranking.

TALLY →

FULL POTENTIAL

HOW LEADERSHIP STYLES WORK TOGETHER

Now that you have identified your leadership style, let's tie it all together by looking at complementary leadership dynamics within pack herds. Linda Kohanov is an expert with understanding leadership dynamics within pack herds. The following information was adapted from her book, *The Five Roles of the Master Header*,[3] and combined with other well-known leadership ideologies. Consider the dynamics of a pack of horses:

L is the VISIONARY that is leading the herd, but also tends to lose sight of the pack because it is too busy looking forward.

E is the NURTURER keeping the pack together, but if everyone was a nurturer the herd wouldn't go anywhere.

A is ANALYTICAL, gathering information from the sides of the pack to create systems that keep the herd safe, but does not like taking risks.

D is ASSERTIVE and is not afraid to give a little nip from behind to keep the herd moving forward, but can sometimes come off as harsh and might have a hard time keeping the pack together.

Leadership is very relevant to the work world. Having a heightened awareness about your leadership style can be helpful with:

- Understanding your strengths and weaknesses
- Obtaining optimal results in a team setting
- Conveying your self-awareness and your understanding of team dynamics when interviewing

The goal is to be able to incorporate all the leadership styles to better equip you to be able to handle different personalities and situations. The more evolved you become, the more you are able to step into all these leadership styles. There will always be traits that are stronger than others. With your least comfortable leadership style, you can either practice building your capacity or ask for help from someone who has that particular leadership strength. Harmony can happen in accepting, understanding, and bringing together a diverse team of leadership styles. The results from collaboration can be fruitful and create a more well-rounded approach to accomplishing shared goals.

CONTEMPLATING LEADERSHIP

What insights have you gained by knowing your leadership style?
Example: That it's okay to not be good at anything and that different people can play different roles.

What are ways you can apply this information in your current work/school situation? Example: I better understand where my co-worker is coming from and can adjust how I approach them - or our team would benefit from an analytical thinker and we should recruit someone to join us.

Would you prefer to improve on your least comfortable leadership style(s), or seek out help from others when those leadership style(s) are needed? How would you go about either (be as specific as possible)? Example: I would prefer to improve my nurturing qualities. I will do this by celebrating wins on the team and being more forgiving with mistakes.

PERSPECTIVE SURVEY

Just as an artist steps back from the canvas to see the painting more clearly, we too should step back to observe ourselves from new perspectives.

- Jacqueline Kramer

INTERVIEW

A great way to build self-awareness is through receiving feedback from others. We all have blind spots. The best people to shine light on those blind spots are the people who we interact with regularly. For this next activity, pick one person who knows you well and schedule a 15-minute call with them to answer the following questions.

Parameters For The Interview
- Only proceed with the interview if you feel capable of receiving feedback without it impacting your relationship.
- Make sure they know you well.
- Make sure they will give honest and constructive feedback.

Interview Questions
Fill in the answers from your interview below:

How would you describe my personality?

What are my three greatest strengths?

What are my three biggest challenges?

What kinds of things have you seen me happy or excited about?

....

....

....

What is something I do that appears effortless?

....

....

....

What are some jobs you think I would be good at?

....

....

....

What tends to hold me back?

....

....

....

How have I impacted or influenced your life?

....

....

....

....

BONUS -- Ask an additional person the same interview questions

VEKITA _____

AUTHENTICITY

Our deepest fear is not that we are inadequate. Our deepest fear is that we are powerful beyond measure. It is our light, not our darkness that most frightens us. Your playing small does not serve the world. There is nothing enlightened about shrinking so that other people won't feel insecure around you. We are all meant to shine as children do. It's not just in some of us; it is in everyone. And as we let our own light shine, we unconsciously give other people permission to do the same. As we are liberated from our own fear, our presence automatically liberates others.

- Marianne Williamson

FULL POTENTIAL

AUTHENTICITY

The goal of this guidebook is to help you live a more authentic life. Being authentic is beneficial to you and the people around you, and supports you in being able to reach your goals. Authenticity takes courage and awareness to master. Don't be afraid to say no to things or people that you don't feel in alignment with. When you have the confidence to do only what is truly aligned with you there will only be room for the right things to come into your life. This is not being selfish, nor is it thoughtless; it is being genuine.

Answer the following questions to your best ability:

What does authenticity mean to you?

_____

_____

_____

_____

Who is someone you view as being authentic and what does it feel like to be around them?

_____

_____

_____

_____

What are some ways that you can encourage others to be more authentic?

_____

_____

_____

_____

Are there areas in your life where you are not being authentic? What is the impact on you and on those around you?

_____

_____

_____

_____

Can you recall a time where you had to be courageous in order to be true to yourself? How did it feel?

_____

_____

_____

_____

How does being authentic make you more effective?

_____

_____

_____

_____

Are there areas in your life where you can be more authentic? How would you do this?

_____

_____

_____

_____

FULL POTENTIAL

WHAT YOU WANT IN YOUR LIFE

The price of anything is the amount of life you exchange for it.

- Henry David Thoreau

WORK-LIFE BALANCE

The Korn Ferry Institute found that overall employee stress levels have risen nearly 20% in three decades.[1] The personal impact includes:

- ° **76% of respondents said workplace stress "had a negative impact on their personal relationships."**
- ° **66% have lost sleep due to work-related stress.**
- ° **16% have quit jobs because stress became too overwhelming.**

To truly thrive, it is essential to examine all aspects of your life. Most people struggle with achieving a work-life balance, which can be exhausting and cause stress. Stress creeps its way into interactions, impacts health (from being irritable or depressed to weakening our immune systems and causing health issues), decreases progress and work outputs, and impacts our overall well-being. The good news is that it doesn't have to be this way. You get to choose how you want to live your life. Additionally, if you are working in a job you enjoy, your stress levels decrease by significant amounts. A series of studies by Gallup found that if a person is in alignment with their talents and interests within their career, it leads to increased productivity[2]...meaning, when people are happy they do better work. This gives them more time within their workday and can even lead to extra time in their personal lives. Furthermore, when stress levels are reduced, people become more present with others and the activities they participate in.

What are the key factors for living a fulfilled life? For me, it is a combination of creating or being productive (work), connection through relationships (friends and family), experiencing the wonders of this world (fun and adventure), and exploring the mysteries of life and elevating my soul's progression (spiritual). Being happy incorporates all aspects of your life, not just work.

What would you want to do to start living your ideal life today? Let's jump in and find out!

FINANCES

Money is a terrible master but an excellent servant.

- P.T. Barnum

BEING INTENTIONAL WITH YOUR MONEY

We are now going to shift gears and look at a very practical and essential part of your life, money. No matter whether you have millions in the bank or are in debt, making a financial plan puts you in control of your money. That is why budgeting is essential for living an optimal life. Contrary to what you may think, a budget is not limiting. A budget fosters intention and prioritizes your spending, which allows you to do more of what you want to do.

Albert Einstein said, "Those who understand money earn it and those that don't, pay it." Your first step in budgeting may be getting out of debt. If you have gone down the rabbit hole of accumulating debt it is hard to get out of it, since interest rates are so incredibly high. Debt not only limits your possibilities and impacts your credit, but it also has a major effect on your mental health and personal life. The good news is you can change this by including monthly payments in your budget to gradually reduce what you owe. Your debt may not be eliminated overnight, but in time it will be and having a plan in place will bring you peace of mind. Once your debt is gone you can then direct the payments you were making to reduce your debt towards savings. With a plan in place you don't have to let money issues stand in the way of creating a life you love.

In the following pages you will gain greater clarity about exactly where your money is going by documenting your current monthly spending. It is important to review your finances is important to do from time to time since budgets actively shift with life and career changes. On the following pages please enter in your current monthly budget. If the template doesn't include costs that are unique to you, include them underneath the appropriate categories and add your unique costs into that section's total.

YOUR MONTHLY BUDGET

HOUSING

Rent/Mortgage Payments	$
Power: Electricity/Gas	$
Water	$
Cell Phone	$
Home Phone/Internet/Television	$
Garbage Removal	$
Cleaning/Maintenance/Repairs	$
Security System/Homeowner Group	$
Home/Rental Insurance	$
Other (Remodeling, Decorating)	$
HOUSING TOTAL PER MONTH	$

FOOD

Eating Out (Restaurants, Fast Food, Take-Out/Delivery)	$
Groceries (Store, Farmers Market)	$
FOOD TOTAL PER MONTH	$

HEALTH

Doctor's Visits, Prescriptions	$
Fitness Costs (Gym, Vitamins, etc.)	$
Medical, Life Insurance	$
HEALTH TOTAL PER MONTH	$

INVESTMENTS

Savings Account	$
Retirement	$
Child's Schooling	$
Own Schooling	$
INVESTMENTS TOTAL PER MONTH	$

TRANSPORTATION

TRANSPORTATION

Car Payments	$
Car Maintenance	$
Car Insurance	$
Gas	$
Tolls	$
Public Transportation	$
TRANSPORTATION TOTAL PER MONTH	$

SUPPORT

SUPPORT

Child Care (Babysitting)	$
Child Support	$
Supporting Parent(s)/Guardian(s)	$
Pet Care	$
Charity or Church	$
SUPPORT TOTAL PER MONTH	$

FUN + PERSONAL CARE

FUN + PERSONAL CARE

Clothes, Shoes, Fashion Accessories, etc.	$
Video Games, Music, Movies, Streaming	$
Magazines and Books	$
Hygiene Products	$
Gifts	$
Vacations/Other Fun Outings	$
FUN + PERSONAL CARE TOTAL PER MONTH	$

OTHER

OTHER

Credit Card Bills	$
Loans	$
Accountant/Taxes	$
Hired Tax Help	$
OTHER TOTAL PER MONTH	$

FULL POTENTIAL

Add in your answers for each category to find out what your monthly budget is. You can multiply this number by twelve to get a sense of what you need to make for an annual salary.

HOUSING	$		SUPPORT	$
TRANSPORTATION	$		INVESTMENT	$
FOOD	$		FUN + PERSONAL CARE	$
HEALTH	$		OTHER	$

GRAND TOTAL (COMBINE ALL)	$

Are there places where you can spend less money?

For example, making coffee at home versus buying coffee at a cafe can save you about $1,000 a year.

....

....

....

....

Are there places where you would like to allocate more money?

For example, saving for a trip or buying a house.

....

....

....

....

YOUR CONNECTION TO MONEY

What drives or limits you from gaining money is usually related to your beliefs. Let's explore your relationship with money.

How much are you motivated by money?

NOT AT ALL | 1 | 2 | 3 | 4 | 5 | 6 | 7 | 8 | 9 | 10 | *THE MOST IMPORTANT THING IN YOUR LIFE*

What life situations and/or people have influenced how you think about money? (family members, significant events, friendships, media, partners, etc.)

FULL POTENTIAL

What does money bring into your life?

For example, peace of mind, support for my family, being able to travel, etc.

_____

_____

_____

_____

_____

_____

_____

_____

What gets financial priority after basic necessities are met?

_____

_____

_____

_____

_____

_____

Is there anything that you need to save money for to help you actualize your ideal job, such as education or cushion money, that would allow you to transition jobs?

....

....

....

....

Does a lack of money interfere with your ability to reach your goals?
If yes, what are some specific ways you can overcome this? For example, if you need funding to create a prototype for a business idea, perhaps you can make passive money through renting out your car or a room in your home. You can also obtain funds through selling items you already have or finding high quality items at thrift stores and sell them in online marketplaces. There are many ways to overcome lack of money as a barrier if you think outside of the box, and pursue your goal in stages that works with your budget.

....

....

....

....

....

....

....

....

....

YOUR IDEAL BUDGET 10 YEARS FROM NOW

Psychologists from Purdue University and the University of Virginia found that the average ideal income for a single adults emotional well-being is $75,000 a year, meaning money will not impact your happiness beyond the 75k threshold.[3] However, we all have different needs and goals.

Take a moment to think about what kind of lifestyle you would like to create in your future. Have you been dreaming of owning a specific type of car? Would you like to live as a digital nomad? Do you want to invest money to generate passive income? Do you want a family with three kids? Do you want to retire and spend money on things you are passionate about?

How do you envision your life will change in the future and how will that impact your finances?

....

....

....

....

You are now going to design a budget that matches your aspirations. In your ideal life budget, you may obtain different things at different times. Think about where you would like to be ten years from now and what your financial situation might be. In your budget you may be putting away money for that dream home or making monthly payments on a Porsche. Make educated guesses for the amount of each section. It does not have to be exact. Dream expansively, but also keep your goals realistic and achievable.

 HOUSING

HOUSING	
Rent/Mortgage Payments	$
Power: Electricity/Gas	$
Water	$
Cell Phone	$
Home Phone/Internet/Television	$
Garbage Removal	$

Cleaning/Maintenance/Repairs	$
Security System/Homeowner Group	$
Home/Rental Insurance	$
Other (Remodeling, Decorating)	$
HOUSING TOTAL PER MONTH	$

FOOD

FOOD

Eating Out (Restaurants, Fast Food, Take-Out/Delivery)	$
Groceries (Store, Farmers Market)	$
FOOD TOTAL PER MONTH	$

HEALTH

HEALTH

Doctor's Visits, Prescriptions	$
Fitness Costs (Gym, Vitamins, etc.)	$
Medical, Life Insurance	$
HEALTH TOTAL PER MONTH	$

INVESTMENTS

INVESTMENTS

Savings Account	$
Retirement	$
Child's Schooling	$
Own Schooling	$
INVESTMENTS TOTAL PER MONTH	$

TRANSPORTATION

TRANSPORTATION

Car Payments	$
Car Maintenance	$
Car Insurance	$
Gas	$
Tolls	$
Public Transportation	$
TRANSPORTATION TOTAL PER MONTH	$

FULL POTENTIAL

SUPPORT

SUPPORT

Child Care (Babysitting)	$
Child Support	$
Supporting Parent(s)/Guardian(s)	$
Pet Care	$
Charity or Church	$
SUPPORT TOTAL PER MONTH	$

FUN + PERSONAL CARE

FUN + PERSONAL CARE

Clothes, Shoes, Fashion Accessories, etc.	$
Video Games, Music, Movies, Streaming	$
Magazines and Books	$
Hygiene Products	$
Gifts	$
Vacations/Other Fun Outings	$
FUN + PERSONAL CARE TOTAL PER MONTH	$

OTHER

OTHER

Credit Card Bills	$
Loans	$
Accountant/Taxes	$
Hired Tax Help	$
OTHER TOTAL PER MONTH	$

Add in your answers for each category to find out what your monthly budget is. You can multiply this number by twelve to get a sense of what you need to make for an annual salary.

HOUSING	$	SUPPORT	$
TRANSPORTATION	$	INVESTMENT	$
FOOD	$	FUN + PERSONAL CARE	$
HEALTH	$	OTHER	$

GRAND TOTAL (COMBINE ALL) $

HOW DO YOU WANT TO FEEL IN YOUR LIFE?

The best and most beautiful things in the world cannot be seen or even touched. They must be felt by the heart.

- Helen Keller

IDENTIFYING EMOTIONS

Life is full of emotions and feelings, but have you ever taken the time to think about what emotions you want more of in your life? Identifying the feelings most important to you offers you the opportunity to work towards increasing them.

Below is a list of words associated with feelings and emotions. Take a moment to review them and circle ones that you relate to. This will help to spark your thoughts before we get started.

Abundant	Devoted	Loving/Loved
Accomplished	Disciplined/Structured	Mindful
Active	Dynamic	Open
Affectionate	Ease	Optimistic
Alive	Energetic	Optimal
Ambitious	Engaged	Passionate
Attuned	Empowered	Peaceful
Awe	Expansive	Playful
Balanced	Fascinated	Powerful
Beautiful/Handsome	Fearless	Receptive
Brave	Free	Relaxed
Bold	Generous	Satisfied
Calm	Genuine	Secure
Certain	Grounded	Sensual
Confident	Happy	Soothed
Connected	Harmonious	Spirited
Content	Healthy	Strong
Courageous	Helpful	Thankful
Challenged	Independent	Trusting
Clever	Inspired	Unique
Creative	Interested	Valued
Daring	Intuitive	Vibrant
Desirable	Important	Whole
Determined	Joyful	Wise

Play with this list and add your own words. You may want to look up the meaning of the words in a dictionary and explore synonyms for this activity.

DESIRED FEELINGS

What are the feelings you would like to increase in your life? To better access your emotions, it may be helpful to close your eyes as you think about these questions.

Write down adjective(s) associated with moments when you were in a great mood or feeling your best:
Example: I felt my best when I was being proactive or helping others or being creative, etc.

_____

_____

_____

_____

_____

_____

How do you want to feel when you are at work?
Example: I want to feel accomplished, relaxed, challenged, etc.

_____

_____

_____

A time I felt like this was: _____

_____

_____

FULL POTENTIAL

How do you want to feel while engaging in your interests?
(Interests may include hobbies, taking classes, being creative, etc.)

Example: I feel inspired when I am volunteering or I feel stimulated in conversations where new knowledge is exchanged, etc.

A time I felt like this was:

How do you want to feel in your personal life?
Example: I want to feel balanced, fulfilled, abundant, etc

A time I felt like this was:

How do you want to feel when you walk into your home, office or other physical space?

Example: I want to feel alive, peaceful, secure, etc.

....

....

....

....

A time I felt like this was:..

....

....

....

How do you want to feel physically?

Example: I want to feel healthy, energized, attractive, etc.

....

....

....

....

A time I felt like this was:..

....

....

....

FULL POTENTIAL

How do you want to feel while interacting with others?
Example: I want to feel joyful, empowered, inspired, etc.

_____

_____

_____

_____

A time I felt like this was:_____

_____

_____

_____

How do you want to feel when you are connecting to something bigger than yourself? (e.g. being in nature, being in service, religion, spirituality, etc.)
Example: I want to feel uplifted, connected, open, etc.

_____

_____

_____

_____

A time I felt like this was:_____

_____

_____

_____

Review the previous section where you identified the feelings you want more of in your life and select the top three feelings you want to increase within the next six months. Write those feelings below. You can always come back to this list at a later date to add other feelings, but you don't want to overwhelm yourself. If you are having a hard time deciding which feelings to choose, you can look at two options side by side and ask yourself if you had to choose just one which one would it be. Continue doing that with your options until you have whittled it down to your top choices.

Looking into the future, what feelings/emotions do you want to increase in your life?

1.

2.

3.

Let's put this into action...

I will increase the feeling of _____ **by**

I will increase the feeling of _____ **by**

I will increase the feeling of _____ **by**

ACTUALIZATION SUGGESTIONS:

- Create a visual representation of the feelings you want to increase in your life. For example, if you want more balance in your life you can include a visual representation of the scales of justice.

- Create a separate page for each feeling: write the word of the feeling, add a picture, and the action(s) you will take to increase this feeling. Place them somewhere you will often see to serve as a reminder.

- Create daily reminders on your phone/computer or on post it notes, of the feelings you want to increase in your life and how you can take action to increase them.

Balance

WORK-LIFE INTEGRATION

Don't get so busy making a living that you forget to make a life.

- Dolly Parton

TIME INVESTMENT

Macro Look

Where are you investing your time and energy? The following ten sections represent different aspects of your life. Rank your level of satisfaction by coloring in the numbers in each category. One (1) is completely dissatisfied and ten (10) is fully satisfied.

Career	1	2	3	4	5	6	7	8	9	10
Money	1	2	3	4	5	6	7	8	9	10
Physical Environment	1	2	3	4	5	6	7	8	9	10
Health and Fitness	1	2	3	4	5	6	7	8	9	10
Fun and Recreation	1	2	3	4	5	6	7	8	9	10
Personal/Professional Development	1	2	3	4	5	6	7	8	9	10
Friends	1	2	3	4	5	6	7	8	9	10
Family	1	2	3	4	5	6	7	8	9	10
Romance	1	2	3	4	5	6	7	8	9	10
Interests	1	2	3	4	5	6	7	8	9	10
Other_____	1	2	3	4	5	6	7	8	9	10

Descriptions for each section:

Career – Do you enjoy your work? Do you feel challenged and engaged? Does your skill set fit with your work? Do you enjoy your co-workers and work environment?

Money – How satisfied are you with your financial status? Are your basic expenses covered? Are you investing and planning for the future? Do you have discretionary money to enjoy life? Are you organized with your money and know what is coming in and what needs to be paid?

Physical environment – How happy are you with the places you spend time in? Your car, home, work, your wardrobe, etc. Is your home decorated and clean or unorganized and messy? How does spending time in these places make you feel?

Health and fitness – How much time are you investing in taking care of your health? Healthy food, regular exercise, taking vitamins, self care (chiropractic treatments, meditating, beauty care), etc.

Fun and recreation – Are you eating at your favorite restaurant, dancing, reading, playing games, going to concerts, traveling, building something, or doing anything else you consider fun?

Personal/professional development – Are you happy with the amount of time you are spending on your career advancement and personal growth? and professional development? Are you expanding who you are by exercising your mind, reading books, going to talks, watching documentaries, gaining skills, going to workshops or retreats, etc.?

Friends – How much time do you spend with close friends? Are you spending time with people that bring out the best in you? Are you wanting to spend time meeting new people and expanding your network?

Family – Are you happy with the amount of time you spend with your family (which can be more or less)? Do you have positive relationships and is spending time together uplifting? Are you holding grudges? Does your family accept you for who you are? Is there room for improving relationships and are your family member(s) willing to put in the time/work to improve relations?

Romance – How much of your energy goes into your romantic life? If you're single, are you wanting to invest time into meeting someone or are you enjoying the single life? If you are in a relationship, is the amount of energy you put into that person reciprocated and is it a healthy relationship? Are you happy with how you're investing your time with your current situation?

Interests – Are you spending time engaging in interests or hobbies? Such as time outdoors, building things, being creative, community engagement, flying a drone, gardening, etc.

FULL POTENTIAL

REFLECTION

If you had to pick one aspect of your life to increase your satisfaction what would that be?

What actions would you take to increase your satisfaction in that specific area?

Micro Look

Being successful is largely determined by your daily routine. Most of us get lost in everyday tasks and feel like we "have" to do certain things. We can't seem to find the time to do the things that are truly meaningful or healthy for us. I get it. I struggle with this one as well. We may think life has to be a certain way, but a lot of the time what we think is unchangeable actually can be changed. This next activity will help you identify where you put your time and where time can be redirected. We have more control of our lives than we think. We are able to make changes, when we know how to make them. When you know exactly what you are doing with your time and are aware of how your daily activities make you feel, you have the power to change.

Track your daily schedule for one week. When tracking your daily routine, begin with the moment you wake up and conclude with the last thing you do before you go to sleep. Write down what you're doing as often as you can. This may include: things you do at work or school, places you visit, extended periods of time you are on your phone, people you interact with, eating, exercising, watching TV, etc. It is important to be honest; for example spending thirty minutes looking at your social media feeds needs to be included.

Document the amount of time you spend on each activity. Doing this can help you figure out where your time is being allocated and where your time can be redirected. For example, I realized I spent eight hours each week watching television. I was able to reallocate three of those hours to exercise, even though I previously thought I didn't have time for that.

You will also be tracking how you feel while you're engaging in these activities. For example, I used to check my phone's notifications first thing in the morning. Immediately, I became overwhelmed by all the messages I had to answer, which left me feeling disconnected from myself. The change I had to make was to buy an alarm clock and put my phone outside of my room at night. Now the first thing I do in the morning is drink a glass of water and stretch. This new routine leaves me feeling grounded, peaceful and energized - gifting me with more energy and focus throughout the day. Becoming aware of how you feel while doing different activities can help you identify areas you may want to change. Tracking how activities make you feel, can also be an excellent indicator for identifying work roles that you might enjoy pursuing.

Download copies of the worksheet for tracking your daily schedule at: **vekitapd.com/resources** After tracking your schedule for a week, review your findings using the guidance of the next activity.

FULL POTENTIAL

ENERGIZED, NEUTRAL AND DEPLETED

Now that you have tracked your schedule for a week, lay out all the pages side by side so you can compare all of your days. Read through all the instructions before you begin. Have colored pens or pencils that you can use and set aside an hour for this activity. You are going to do three things:

1. In your daily schedules, categorically group activities by color coding them. Create the types of groupings that best represent your lifestyle and the activities you do most. An example of how to do this activity is: (circle) all work related activities in green or all health activities in blue. Identifying categories helps you better understand the amount of time you are spending within the different parts of your life.

2. On the following pages, place what you did from each of the days into the appropriate bucket (draining, neutral or energizing). Write each activity into the appropriate bucket with the color pen that represents the categorical grouping which it falls into.

Next to the name of the activity write the total amount of time that you spent doing this activity throughout the week. For example, if I spent a total of five hours that week working out and I felt energized about the experience, I would write in the energized bucket," Exercise 5h"- and I would write it in blue to tag it as health related.

You may find that the same activity can fall into different buckets. For example, if I have eight one hour meetings throughout the week, and three out of eight meetings left me feeling drained I would write "meetings 3h" in the depleted bucket and tag it by the color I assigned to work, which in the previous example is green. If the other meetings were all uplifting I would place the remaining hours in the energized bucket, labeling it in green "meetings 5h."

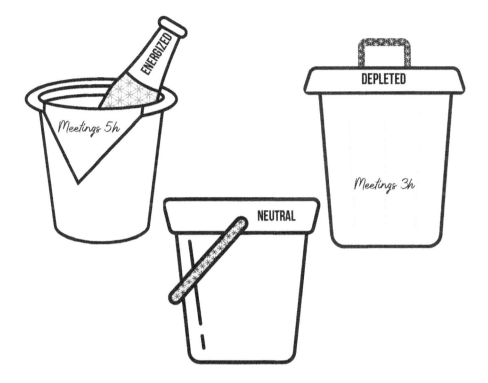

After you have placed all your activities into the buckets, add up the total time spent in each bucket. This will help you get a realistic idea of where your time and energy is going, and possible shifts you may want to make.

3. Finally, see if you can find patterns related to why you felt the way you did with your daily activities. For some activities the answer may be straightforward, such as exercising leaves me feeling energized because I feel proud that I took the time to do good things for my mental and physical health. If you find that the same activity fell into different buckets, like the above example of the meetings, see if you can find out why the pattern differentiated. For example, it could have been the people you had meetings with or maybe it was the content that left you feeling a specific way. Make a note of any patterns that feel significant to you.

FULL POTENTIAL

ENERGIZED

TOTAL TIME:

VEKITA

NEUTRAL

DEPLETED

TOTAL TIME:

CHOOSING WHERE TO SPEND YOUR TIME

Knowledge has the power to inspire change, but knowledge needs to be harnessed and actualized to have any kind of impact. Think of knowledge as a tool in your shed. That tool may be well-built and mighty, giving you the ability to create all kinds of things...if you learn how to use it and put it into action. Otherwise your tool, or the knowledge you gained, stays dormant. Knowledge is just knowledge, until you put it into action, then knowledge is power. Just like a tool, once you have knowledge it in your possession you can always grab it out of the "shed" when the time is right to use it.

If you want to gain more insights around how you are managing your time, it may be beneficial to track your activities for more than a week to get a more robust picture of where you are placing your energy. Another practice you can do is to take a couple minutes each day to journal about the things you did that left you feeling energized. Identifying what brings you energy, essentially places you in a state of flow, which enables you to be hyper focused, fully involved and enjoying the process of that activity. Optimizing your time, and doing more of what makes you feel energized, can lead to a more fulfilling, successful, and impactful life.

Where would you like to be spending less time?

Where would you like to be investing more time?

FULL POTENTIAL

HABITS

People do not decide their futures, they decide their habits and their habits decide their futures.

- F.M. Alexander

CREATING NEW HABITS

Forty percent of daily actions are based on habits. Changing your habits can significantly impact your life and your ability to reach your goals. It's important to look at the whole picture of the habits you incorporate into your life. This includes: eating healthy, sleep, exercising, and your emotional well-being. Your energy and mental sharpness are directly tied to living your full potential.

In *The Power of Habit* by Charles Duhigg[4] he identifies four phases in the neurological feedback loop that all habits are subject to:

Cue- what triggers your habit, example: you get off of work ->

Craving - what fuels your habit, example: you want to feel fit ->

Response - what you do, example: you go to the gym ->

Reward - what you get, example: your craving is satisfied by feeling fit, or maybe you want to give yourself a tangible reward such as, after exercising for a week you get a scoop of your favorite ice cream.

Disrupting any one of the elements within the cycle can create a new reaction, which can change a habit. One of the best ways to disrupt or form a habit is to change or create a new cue. Know what the cue is and be prepared with a plan. Staying with the gym example, before leaving the office you can change into exercise clothes. If your first plan for changing a habit doesn't work you can try another tactic.

An essential element that I feel is missing in this model is **support**. For example, programs that are designed to help you quit a bad habit, such as Alcoholics Anonymous, assign sponsors. Support can come in many forms. If you are wanting to get fit, support may come through working out with a friend, hiring a personal trainer, or going to a specific workout class.

If you want to create new habits, ask yourself:
• How can I make the cue obvious?
• How can I make the craving attractive?
• How can I make the response easy?
• How can I make the reward satisfying?
• How can I create a support system?

CHANGING A HABIT

You now have clarity of where you are investing your time and energy. You may have found there are elements of your daily routine that you want to shift to better reflect your priorities and ensure your success. This may include changing or altering a habit.

What is a habit you would like to alter or get rid of?

What is driving your motivation (your "why") for wanting to change this habit?

What is the cue for when this habit occurs?

What can you do in response of the cue, instead of doing this habit?

How can you make the alternate activity rewarding and satisfying?

What support systems can you put in place to help you change this habit?

CREATING A NEW HABIT

Creating habits to support your goals and well-being will make you more effective and successful. Scheduling time on your calendar is a great way to hold space to do the things that are important to you and to create the opportunity for change. You might also want to explore apps that can assist you with forming new habits and managing daily routines.

What habit would you would like to add into your life?

....

What is driving your motivation (your "why") for creating this new habit?

....

....

What is a cue to do this new habit? Something noticeable that will bring your awareness to doing this new habit.

....

....

What will you do in response to the cue? What you do the moment the cue happens.

....

....

What will make the reward of doing this new habit satisfying? Something that provides pleasure and motivation.

....

....

What support systems can you put in place to help you embed this habit?

....

FULL POTENTIAL

IMPACT

Helping one person may not change the world, but it can change the world for that person.

- Unknown

HOW DO YOU WANT
TO MAKE A DIFFERENCE IN THE WORLD?

Making a difference in the world can come in many forms. It may be as simple as living a happy life or wanting to raise children who will be wiser and smarter than you. It could also be that you want to create a product that impacts peoples lives or be a part of an organization making a difference. What kind of footprint would you like to leave on the world?

I want to make a difference in the world by:

This is important to me because:

I will do this by:

Are there other ways would you like to contribute to individuals or society?

FULL POTENTIAL

IN TIMES OF CRISIS

In the past I have used the same framework you just went through to help people get clear on how they can employ their unique gifts to contribute during times of disaster or chaos. For example, if there is a fire in your area and you are skilled at cooking, you can make meals for the fire victims, or if you are highly networked you can raise money or get supplies. There are many many ways we can help during times of need. Due to disasters feeling out of our control, most people, understandably, tend to get overwhelmed and shut down. Knowing what you are good at can guide you to identify how you can help. During a disaster, ask yourself:

1. Who is being affected? What do they need? The best thing is to find a way to ask them versus what you think they need -- social media is a great tool that can help you find people to ask.

2. Who is already helping and how can I support them? Check out organizations that are local to the area and have good reputations.

3. Are goods and supplies needed? Can I send things or money to support? Do I have resources that can help (temporary housing, clothing, etc.)?

4. Who are the key influencers who can make a change now and in the future (government, legal, community, etc.)?

5. Is there any hands-on help that is needed (building structures, cooking, healthcare, etc.)?

There are many ways to create positive change in the world. Some people may choose social impact careers that have positive effects on individuals and/or society. Others may choose to contribute outside of work through volunteering or donating money to causes they care about (this too can create substantial impact). Elizabeth Hopper from U.C. Berkeley's Greater Good Science Center identified research concluding that being kind and giving to others can make our lives feel more meaningful[5] So as you make others happy, you are in turn also increasing your own happiness as well.

MIDWAY REFLECTION

You have made it halfway through the steps of identifying your career and life goals.

How are you feeling?

You have been identifying what you want in work and life, but what are some things you absolutely do not want (think about things that cause you stress)?

What have you learned that stands out to you the most?

FULL POTENTIAL

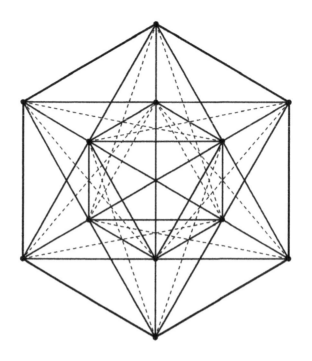

ALIGNING WHO YOU ARE WITH CAREERS

New beginnings are often disguised as painful endings.

- Lao Tzu

CONNECTING YOUR UNIQUE BLUEPRINT TO JOBS

If you are currently in a role where you feel stagnant or want a change, you may just need a couple small tweaks to increase job satisfaction. For others, you will want a complete refresh and will be changing careers, or maybe this is your first job. The previous sections offered greater awareness and clarity into who you are, your interests, and strengths. For the next step, you will pair what you've learned about yourself with job options, in order to identify your ideal role.

Understanding the foundation of who you are serves as a framework, providing structure and tools to use when considering future career or life changes. Knowing yourself allows you to adapt easily to new situations. In the future, there will be jobs created that never existed before. You may also gain new perspectives and skills, or experience shifts within your personal life, that could influence your career choices. You can choose to revisit this framework at any time. Some of you may stick with one career in your life. Others will have a handful of careers. One career or many careers can both lead to a fulfilling life. What you gain from doing this work is that you will not be stumbling into your career, which may or may not be in alignment with you. Instead you will be in control of your career path and living with more ease and congruency.

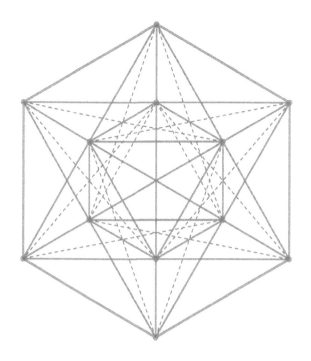

ENVISIONING YOUR IDEAL LIFE

Dreaming is a form of planning. Envisioning what you want sets your dreams into motion to become actualized.

- Nicole Serena Silver

LIMITLESS

If you had a year to live with no financial limitations or personal obligations then...

How would you spend your time?

What would you do within your personal life and what would change?

If you knew you would be successful, what would you want to accomplish with your career?

Even with the risk of failure what would you still want to do?

FULL POTENTIAL

IDEAL LIFE VISUALIZATION

Many successful people use visualization as a tool. Visualization can be used to "practice" something in a low-risk way, imagine outcomes, increase focus on a goal, and act as a guide to becoming clearer about your future. The following visualization gives you the opportunity to dream and imagine what it would be like to live a day in your ideal life. Set aside twenty undisturbed minutes in a quiet space. Have colored pens or pencils available to you to access after the visualization ends.

STEP 1 - Visit: **vekitapd.com/resources** for the visualization.

STEP 2 - After you have listened to the visualization, please take at least ten minutes to journal, draw or express in any form you'd like about what came up for you during the visualization in the space below.

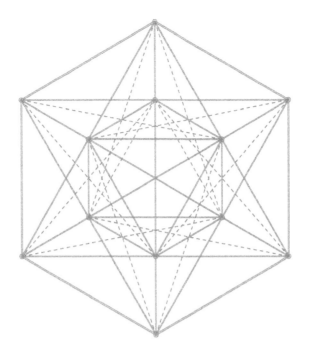

WRITING YOUR IDEAL
JOB DESCRIPTION

*The best way to predict
the future is to create it.*

- Abraham Lincoln

YOUR IDEAL JOB DESCRIPTION

You now get to take the information you have learned about yourself and use it to write out your ideal job description. It is rewarding to watch how all the work you have done culminates. **On a blank piece of paper write your answers to the questions below.** You will write your completed job description after you have brainstormed your answers. Let's get started!

Section 1: Create a descriptive title

Come up with a clear and short title to describe your ideal role. What are the top two or three words you would use to describe yourself?

Examples:

- Creative people person
- Compassionate and strategic collaborator
- Lively, dedicated communicator
- Trustworthy, determined motivator
- Passionate, likeable caregiver
- Hard-working, supportive youth leader

Section 2: You'll love this job if...

Write up a short statement about the qualities you care about in a job. Your previous passion, personality, and values notes might be helpful.

Prompts:

- You are passionate about...
- You value...
- You're really good at...
- You're a _____, _____ person

Examples:

- You are passionate about both technology and healthcare
- You like traveling a lot
- You have a sense of humor and like to have fun (you work hard, but you laugh a lot too!)
- You enjoy having different tasks at once and don't like routine
- Growth and learning is important to you

Section 3: Responsibilities

Think about your interactions with others. Your previous leadership style notes might be helpful.

Prompts:
- Do you like to manage people or be given directions?
- How many people would you like to interact with on a daily basis?
- Do you like working independently or with a team?
- Do you like to work more with your hands or with computers?
- Do you like to come up with new ideas, or do you prefer to be the one who brings the idea to life?

Examples:
- You are a manager responsible for supervising and guiding a team
- You are a self-starter who completes tasks independently
- You are data-driven and check that projects are meeting their goals
- You are a creative problem-solver thinking up solutions

Section 4: List skills

List your soft and hard skills which you have identified. You can also add any skills you plan on acquiring.

Prompts:
- Do you adapt to change quickly? Are you a people-person, or a good email writer?
- Do you need to speak a foreign language, to type fast, or to have a degree or certificate?
- Do you need to be skilled at using particular tools like software, hand tools, electric tools, or other types of tools?

Examples:
- Excellent communication skills both written and verbal
- Microsoft Office experience

FULL POTENTIAL

Section 5: Describe a workday

Think about what you would do on a typical day. The previous ideal life visualization may have been helpful with envisioning your routine.

Prompts:
- What time do you go to work?
- What time do you get out of work?
- How many days a week do you go?
- How long and how often are your breaks?
- What things do you do regularly/daily?
- What do you do occasionally?

Examples:
- You work a stable 9AM-5PM five-day week
- You work around the needs of a project or task
- You regularly travel to meet with clients

YOUR IDEAL JOB DESCRIPTION

Write your complete job description below:

YOUR IDEAL JOB DESCRIPTION CONT.

FULL POTENTIAL

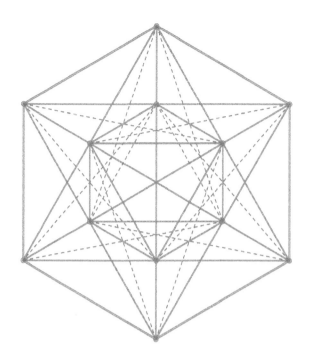

JOB
SUGGESTIONS

*"The way to get good ideas
is to get lots of ideas and
throw the bad ones away.*

- Linus Pauling

EXPLORING OPTIONS

You may find there are many possibilities for career paths that could be a good match for you. Explore as many jobs as you can and later you will narrow them down. For now just play with all the possibilities. Don't feel the need to make any decision and let your mind relax through this process. Have fun, be creative and explore different options without needing to figure anything out.

JOB PAIRINGS RELATED TO YOUR STRENGTHS

The following sections pair your strengths (which you learned in the "Who You Are" chapter) with jobs. These suggestions are based on patterns of characteristics that work well with the tasks related to each job. It is also possible that a job in a category unrelated to your top strength might be a good fit for you. There are no absolute rules, only suggestions. The suggested jobs can also be used as a catalyst to spark thoughts of possible jobs not mentioned in the lists. For example, you may see "marriage counselor" and it might spark other forms of counseling, such as helping troubled children. Keep your mind open during this process and think outside of the box.

If you find any of the following jobs interesting, **check or circle** them so you can explore them at a later point in the guidebook. Those of you who feel clear about your ideal industry or sector, but want to narrow down specific roles or level up with your current career, can also find value in this section. You may gain inspiration for the next steps in your current career or you may discover something completely new that you would like to explore. Play with lots of possibilities and don't worry about figuring anything out at the moment.

JOBS RELATED TO YOUR SKILLS

SOCIAL INTERACTION
Skills that incorporate working with individuals or groups

HUMAN INTERACTION
Collaboration, high social/ cultural sensitivity, and conflict resolution

Creates and maintains good working relationships

Employee Relations Representative builds employee-management relations
Diversity, Equity and Inclusion recognizes, creates and implements plans to promote diversity within an organisation
Mediator resolves legal conflicts between two people or organizations
Sales Represenative sells a product(s) or service related to clients needs
Social Worker helps individuals, families, groups and communities to enhance their individual and collective well-being
Marriage Counselor counsels couples
Operations Manager oversees the daily operations of an organization

SERVICE
Provides care and support, communicates between people or organizations, serves clients and customers, and supports cause(s)

Actively seeks ways to enhance the wellbeing and happiness of clients, customers, and the enviornment

Rehabilitation Physician helps patients with serious physical/mental injuries recover
Customer Success develops customer relationships that promote retention and loyalty
Case Manager creates and manages the overall plan of care for patients
Community Relations Officer builds community-organization relationships
Licensed Realtor helps people purchase homes
Flight Attendant ensures the safety and comfort of passengers aboard flights
Technology Consultant helps businesses and people figure out what technologies work best for efficentcy and their needs

COUNSEL/TEACH
Guides people in a group to work together to reach a goal, counsels, and trains/teaches

Develops and helps people and groups reach personal and professional goals

Art/Music Therapist uses art or music for theraputic purposes
Project Manager manages teams for the planning, procurement and execution of a project
Product Manager Leads the launch of products
Genetics Counselor counsels patients on genetic diseases
Career Coach Guides individuals through the job alignment and actualization process
Childbirth Educator provides support and trains parents-to-be
Healthcare Navigator teaches patients and their loved ones about the ins and outs of a complicated medical system

COMMUNICATION

C Strong verbal and written communication skills for interaction with individuals, groups, and/or the public

VERBAL/WRITTEN

Listens, speaks, interacts, and writes

Exchanges information through verbal, written, or non-verbal cues

Publicist Advertises people or products through press releases, tours, and other means
Motivational Speaker speaks to motivate crowds
Senior Technical Writer writes about differnet products
Space Science Journalist writes articles/blogs about space sciences
News Anchor delivers news on television
Nurse Practitioner caregivers with strong core communication skills
Socal Media Manager grows businesses through social networks by improving website traffic and optimizing brand awareness

PERSUASION/PROMOTION

Convinces, advertises, sells, and speaks to groups

Uses information, ideas, and guidance to get a desired outcome

Attorney represents people/organizations in legal matters
Copywriter writes materials for advertising
Grant Writer writes grant to obtain funding for organizations
Media Buyer purchases space for advertising based on identified client fit
Agent/Business Manager of Artists represents and manages the business of artists
Lead Prospector and Sales builds targeted lead list and procures clients
Internet Personality/Influencer a personality or specialist on social media platforms, such as a YouTuber

CONSULTATION/INFLUENCE

Guides people or organizations, researches and studies their needs, and comes up with suggested solutions

Works with others to find problems, develops solutions and provides advice

Community Relations Specialist builds community-organization relationships
Executive Coach guides executives with personal and professional development
Mediator helps resolve conflicts between disputing parties
Strategy Consultant works with business executives to apply business strategies
Market Researcher helps businesses find out what people think about their product
User Experience Researcher replaces guesswork with informed insights to improve users' experience with products or services
Political Consultant consults and guides political parties

FULL POTENTIAL

ORGANIZATIONAL MANAGEMENT

Plans, implements, manages/organizes, and makes sure things run smoothly

Plans and takes steps to complete projects and tasks

Event Manager organizes events
Instructional Coordinator designs school and district education curriculum
IT Project Manager plans, initiates, and manages computer-related activities
Art Director manages the overall art in a tv series/movie/exhibition
Organizational Effectiveness Consultant helps a business evaluate its operations and suggests changes in the process
Construction Superintendent plans, coordinates, budgets, and supervises construction projects from start to finish
Quality Control Manager ensures that a product is of good quality

MENTORING/TEAM MANAGEMENT

Builds a team, coaches, and sets goals

Motivates people and groups for greater participation, commitment, and better performance

First-Line Supervisor manages the emergency action team
Fundraising Manager plans and manages donations
Labor Relations Manager manages relations between employees and managers
Film Producer plans and coordinates all parts of the film
Doula provides guidance and support to a pregnant woman before, during and after labor
Leadership Coach provides guidance for managers and leaders
Training and Development Manager ensures the development of employees within a company

LEADERSHIP

Imagines a different/better world, leads, and makes decisions

Creates a vision and motivates others to achieve excellence in performance

Administrator manages programs in institutions such as education, hospitals, etc.
Community Development Manager builds community-organization relationships
Army General has the responsibility to make certain decisions which will affect national security and peoples lives
Executive Director Manages a nonprofit organization
Mayor municipal officer in a city or town
Choreographer coordiates dance routines
Biomedical Engineer responsible for innovative designs such as artificial organs and devices that substitute for human body parts

ANALYSIS/PROBLEM SOLVING
*Makes sense of pieces of
information, researches and
solves problems*

Identifies and defines problems
and solutions

Business Analyst uses numbers to help plan the next-steps in a business
Forensic Detective uses biological clues to determine suspects in a crime
Geneticist studies genes
Sustainability Specialist helps businesses design environmentally friendly products
Bioinformatics Specialist uses computer softwares to solve biological problems
Finacial Advisor helps people manage money to build a good financial future
Simplicity Expert Simplifies businesses and streamlines business operations

INFORMATION/DATA MANAGEMENT
*Categorizes, evaluates, and
manages pieces of information*

Collects, manages, and uses
data for more efficient planning

Archaeologist studies and classifies old objects/structures
Machine Learning Senior Data Analyst helps machines learn faster
Insurance Underwriter checks if people can get insurance
Merchandiser ensures that products get to the right store at the correct time and with the correct quantities
Senior Data Analyst converts data into useful information
Human Resource Analyst analyzes employee data within a company
Data Scientist Analyzes large quantities of data using a mixture of complex algorithms and mathematics

COMPUTATIONAL/QUANTITATIVE
*Calculates, estimates, and makes
predictions*

Performs calculations using math
and numbers for predictions and
providing useful information

Auditor reviews the accounts of companies to ensure the validity of their financial records
Cost Estimator finds out how much a product should cost
Energy Auditor makes sure organizations follow energy rules
Financial Anyalist provides guidance to businesses and individuals making investment decisions
Operations Research Analyst helps organizations find better ways to do things in order to save time and money
Criminologist scientific analysis of crime and response to evidence
Computational Biologist develops software to solve biology problems

FULL POTENTIAL

INNOVATIVE

I

Processes, generates, and connects ideas
and information into something new

INTUITIVE

*Uses instinct of what one feels
to understand what's missing or
needed to generate solutions
and new ideas*

Acts upon insights, perceptions,
and observations

Brand Manager builds trust among the public about organizations' work
Surgeon medical practitioner qualified to practice surgery
Psychologist helps people deal with difficult life situations
Mergers & Acquisitions analysis and modeling to support buying, selling, restructuring, and combining companies
Palliative Care Physician cares for dying patients
Political Scientist deals with systems of governance, and the analysis of political activities, political thoughts, and political behaviors
Engagement Marketing advertising strategy that focuses on creating an experience to have customers engage with the brand

INVENTIVE

*Comes up with a concept/idea
and figures out how to make the
idea become a reality.*

Forms structures, patterns, and
connections from information,
ideas, and inspirations

Entreprenur creates, organizes, and operates a business or businesses
Food Scientist studies food, creates alternative solutions and enhances natural farming solutions
Architect designs buildings and structures
Space Suit Design Engineer designs space suits for astronauts
Nostalgist interior designer specializing in recreating memories for retired people
Virtual Reality Designer designs virtual reality games
Industrial Designer combines art, business, and engineering to develop the concepts for manufactured products

ARTISTIC/AESTHETIC

Compose, create, and perform

Transforms inner ideas into
artistic and creative forms

Art Director manages the overall art in a tv series/movie/exhibition
Greensman/Greenswoman builds plant sets for tv/films
Animator makes 2D/3D animated designs
Product Developer develops products for organizations
Video Game Developer makes video games
Hard Modeler Works with all types of materials (wood, plastic, metal, 3D printing, etc.) to make models of things like cars, characters, art, functional tools, etc.
Music Composer writes music for films/video games/tv/orchestras

TECHNICAL

T

Uses the body with physical objects; including machines and technological systems

VISUAL/MOTOR
Hand-eye coordination, athletics, and builds

Uses hands and the body with skill

Wind Turbine Technician designs and maintains the fans and motors in wind mills
Kinesiotherapist helps people with sports injuries
Commercial Pilot flies passenger planes
Medical Equipment Operator operates machines used in hospitals/labs
Video Game QA Testing responsible for finding and reporting bugs in games
Stunt Preformer highly trained professional, contracted to perform dangerous scenes in films, television, and live shows
Landscaper builds and maintains gardens, parks, and other outdoor landscapes

BUILD/STRUCTURE
Builds, renovates, and designs

Assembles a product, building, object, or returns something to its original state

Garbage Designer find ways to turn the by-products of the manufacturing process into high-quality materials for new products
Computer Aided Drafter helps draw designs using special computer software
Aquaponic Fish Farmer combines fish farming with gardening, where plants grow over water to cover its surface, while fish live below
Automotive Engineer designs and builds cars
Industrial Designer creates physical products and goods
Re-wilder undoes environmental damage caused by people, factories, cars, etc.
Prop Maker creates props and masks for movies and theater productions

EQUIPMENT/TECHNOLOGY
Tests, installs, operates equipment, and repairs

Properly uses tools, hardware, software, and machines

Machine Learning Engineer develops algorithms to allow machines to automate decisions and data processing
Audiologist studies sound systems to help people hear
Computer Network Support Specialist makes sure that computer networks work properly
Envioronmental Engineer uses the principles of engineering, soil based biology, and chemistry to develop solutions to environmental problems
Electrical Technician repairs electric equipment
Radiologic Technician takes care of machines used by doctors to treat/detect cancer
Solar Technology Solar instalation

FULL POTENTIAL

JOBS RELATED TO YOUR PERSONALITY

 Perfectionist

You are interested in being correct and fair. You will enjoy doing things the right way and making improvements in your workplace.

- ☐ Advertising Copywriter
- ☐ Aerospace Engineer
- ☐ Anesthesiologist
- ☐ Ecologist
- ☐ Mathematician
- ☐ Operations Research
- ☐ Government Affairs Rep.
- ☐ Conservation Scientist and Forester

Helper

You are interested in helping others. You will enjoy working with people, creating good working enviornments, and having uplifting interactions.

- ☐ Art Therapist
- ☐ Foreign Diplomat
- ☐ Wildlife biologist
- ☐ Translator
- ☐ Occupational Therapist
- ☐ Anesthesiologist
- ☐ Personal Financial Advisor
- ☐ Veterinarian

Achiever

You are interested in achieving your goals. You will enjoy climbing the ladder of success in your career.

- ☐ Business Executive
- ☐ Investment Banker
- ☐ Data Scientist
- ☐ Emergency Management Specialist
- ☐ Sales Manager
- ☐ Professor
- ☐ Real Estate Agent
- ☐ Director of the Environmental Protection Agency

Type 4 — The Individualist

You are interested in being creative. You will enjoy bringing your ideas to life in the workplace.

- ☐ Architect
- ☐ Art Director
- ☐ Entrepreneur
- ☐ Interior Designer
- ☐ Fashion Stylist
- ☐ Film and Media Editor
- ☐ Design Engineer
- ☐ Journalist

Type 5 — The Observer

You are interested in learning and innovation. You will enjoy thinking and discovering new things in your career.

- ☐ A.I. Architect
- ☐ Biochemist/Biophysicist
- ☐ Computer Programmer
- ☐ Environmental Scientist
- ☐ Forensic Scientist
- ☐ Cartographer
- ☐ Market Research Analyst
- ☐ Hydrologist

Type 6 — The Skeptic

You are interested in solving difficult problems. You will enjoy using your skill of tracking patterns in your job.

- ☐ Attorney
- ☐ Computer Forensics
- ☐ Industrial Designer
- ☐ Environmental Specialist
- ☐ Economist
- ☐ Social Media Strategist
- ☐ Legal Arbitrator
- ☐ White Hat Hacker

FULL POTENTIAL

Type 7 — The Enthusiast

You are interested in having fun and new experiences with your work. You will enjoy having a job with variation in an exciting environment.

- ☐ Airline Pilot
- ☐ Consultant
- ☐ Event Planner
- ☐ Hospitality Manager
- ☐ Public-Relations Specialist
- ☐ User Experience Designer
- ☐ Toy Designer
- ☐ Writer/Author

Type 8 — The Challenger

You are interested in being in charge. You will enjoy making important decisions and fighting for the rights of others.

- ☐ Athlete
- ☐ Judge
- ☐ Military Officer
- ☐ Nonprofit Exec Director
- ☐ Athletic Trainer
- ☐ Project Coordinator
- ☐ Social Services Manager
- ☐ Urban Planner

Type 9 — The Peacemaker

You are interested in encouraging others to get along. You will enjoy working at your own pace in a stress-free workplace.

- ☐ Exploration Geologist
- ☐ Furniture Designer
- ☐ Marine Biologist
- ☐ Human Resource Manager
- ☐ Dietician/Nutritionist
- ☐ Underwater Welder
- ☐ Veterinarian
- ☐ Video Game Tester

JOBS RELATED TO YOUR LEADERSHIP STYLE

LEADERSHIP STYLE (L)

- ☐ Aerospace Engineer
- ☐ Athletic Recruiter
- ☐ Automotive Designer
- ☐ Architect
- ☐ Art Director
- ☐ Business Consultant
- ☐ Civil Engineer
- ☐ Drone Pilot
- ☐ Entrepreneur
- ☐ Fashion Designer
- ☐ Marketing Director
- ☐ Movie Set Designer
- ☐ Multimedia Animator
- ☐ Product manager
- ☐ Public Relations Specialist
- ☐ Training and Development
- ☐ Urban Planner
- ☐ Virtual Reality Game Designer

LEADERSHIP STYLE (E)

- ☐ Arbitrator/Mediator
- ☐ Diversity Officer
- ☐ Event Planner
- ☐ Flight Attendant
- ☐ Health Coach
- ☐ Human Resource Manager
- ☐ Hospitality Manager
- ☐ Nonprofit Program Manager
- ☐ Nurse Practitioner
- ☐ Occupational Therapist
- ☐ Physical Therapist
- ☐ Purchasing Manager
- ☐ Recruiter
- ☐ Sales Representative
- ☐ Speech Writer
- ☐ Social Services Manager
- ☐ User Experience Designer
- ☐ Human/Robot
  Interaction Specialist

LEADERSHIP STYLE (A)

- ☐ Actuary/Statistician
- ☐ Air-Traffic Controller
- ☐ Anthropologist
- ☐ Biochemist/Biophysicist
- ☐ Corporate Development
- ☐ Technical Writer
- ☐ Computer Network Architect
- ☐ (Digital) Detective
- ☐ Economist
- ☐ Forensic Science Technician
- ☐ Geographic Information Systems
- ☐ Computer Programmer
- ☐ Environmental Scientist
- ☐ Internet Security Analyst
- ☐ Mass Spectrometry Scientist
- ☐ Operations Analyst
- ☐ Professor
- ☐ Compensations And Benefits
  Manager

LEADERSHIP STYLE (D)

- ☐ Business Executive
- ☐ Business Operations Specialist
- ☐ Construction Manager
- ☐ Hospital Administrator
- ☐ Investment Banker
- ☐ Media Producer/Director
- ☐ Mergers/Acquisitions Manager
- ☐ Lobbyist
- ☐ Military Officer
- ☐ Nonprofit Executive Director
- ☐ Personal Financial Advisor
- ☐ Personal Fitness Trainer
- ☐ Politician
- ☐ Real Estate Agent
- ☐ Sales Person
- ☐ Stock or Options Trader
- ☐ Talent Agent
- ☐ Venture Capitalist

FULL POTENTIAL

CONNECTED JOBS

Place all of the jobs you found interesting below and brainstorm related jobs that you would enjoy. For example, if I found interesting "food scientist," some related jobs may be: biologist working on fruit genetics, bioengineer, biomedical engineer, chef, culinary ambassador, etc. It is possible you may not know the specific job title, but have an idea of what the role might be. For example, if I didn't know the title of "biologist working on fruit genetics" I could write, "food scientist that combines different fruits to make new fruits." If you don't know the title of the job, you can write the description of the role. What suggested jobs have inspired you?

INTRIGUING JOBS

RELATED JOBS

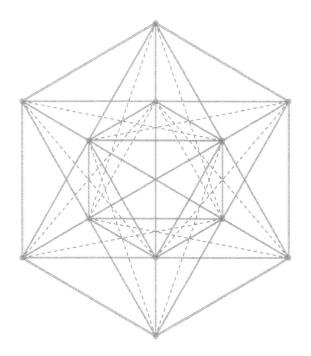

MIND MAPPING

Creativity is intelligence having fun.

- Albert Einstein

When you are experimenting, with anything, the best thing to do is to let your mind relax and try many things before making a choice. Let's explore job possibilities by bringing together the following elements you completed in previous sections: passion (pg.28), skills (pg. 32), values (pg.44), leadership style (pg.55) and impact (pg.102). Fill in the prompts, on the page after next, for each element.

After you have filled in the prompts, then(Circle)any commonalities across all elements. For easy tracking use a different colored pen for each commonality grouping.

Commonality = <u>enjoy working with people</u>

Passion = helping people

Skills = good listener

Leadership = nurturer

Value = working in collaboration

Value = good communication

You may find a commonality does not encompass all the elements. The example above does not include the element of "impact." Also, numerous answers within an element may fit within a commonality grouping (the example above has two "values" within the commonality of "enjoy working with people."

Next, you will want to cluster elements that would work well together into potential job categories. This does not mean clustering commonalities; you already did that. This means using a combination of imagination and logic to find overarching themes that can fit into job categories. You are not looking for specific job titles, just the general categorization. For example:

Skills = graphic design

Leadership = visionary

Passion = being creative and making art

Impact = make useful products that thousands of people use

Categories within this cluster could be: graphic designer, entrepreneur, product development, UX/UI developer, app designer, etc. I intentionally left out "value" to show the variations of combinations, and not all of them need to include all five elements. You can also refer back to the section on passion and skills overlap for an additional example.

VEKITA _____

MIND MAP EXAMPLE

Clustering Potential Jobs

Graphic design
Visionary
Being creative
Making art
Makes useful products that thousands of people use

=

Graphic designer, entrepreneur, product development within a company, UX/UI developer, app designer

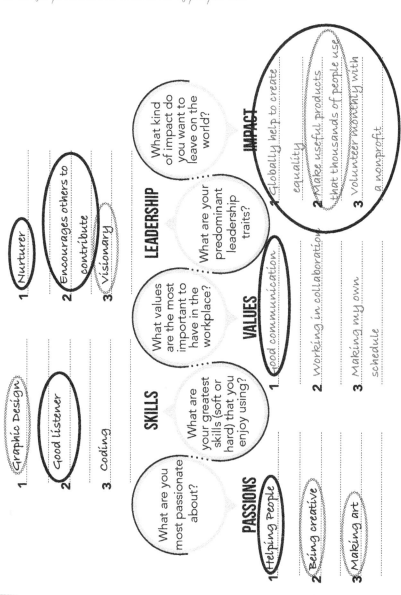

IMPACT
What kind of impact do you want to leave on the world?
1 Globally help to create equality
2 Make useful products that thousands of people use
3 Volunteer monthly with a nonprofit

LEADERSHIP
What are your predominant leadership traits?
1 Nurturer
2 Encourages others to contribute
3 Visionary

VALUES
What values are the most important to have in the workplace?
1 Good communication
2 Working in collaboration
3 Making my own schedule

SKILLS
What are your greatest skills (soft or hard) that you enjoy using?
1 Graphic Design
2 Good listener
3 Coding

PASSIONS
What are you most passionate about?
1 Helping People
2 Being creative
3 Making art

FULL POTENTIAL

YOUR MIND MAP

After you have filled out the sections below, circle commonalities.
When exploring careers:

- Withhold criticism
- Move out of trying to figure things out
- Be playful, dream big, and welcome unconventional ideas
- Try lots of combinations

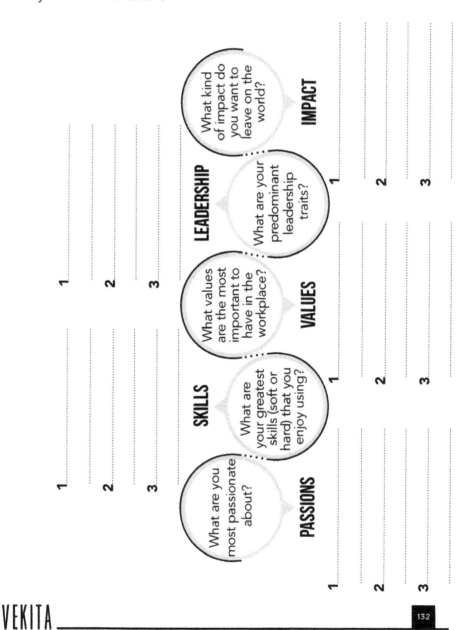

CLUSTERING POTENTIAL JOBS

What categorization of jobs are you the most excited to explore?

FULL POTENTIAL

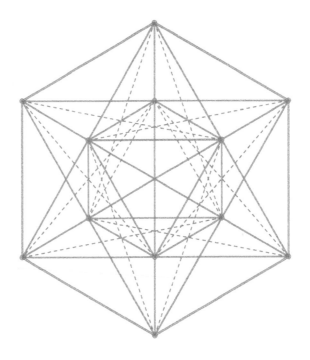

RESEARCHING
JOB TITLES

Research is the distance between an idea and its realization.

- David Sarnoff

TRANSFORMING CATEGORIES INTO JOB TITLES

Now it's time to take the categories you discovered in the previous sections (as well as any jobs you've found interesting in the past) and **research related job titles**. A category is something like engineering and related job titles could be Mechanical Design Engineer Specialist or R&D Optics Engineer. Below are two ways to do your research that have proved to be effective.

When doing research:

- Look past the job title. See what the actual tasks are of the job.
- Expand your search and look at different jobs by exploring similar titles.

Option 1: Use an online search tool, like Google, and type in "_____Category_____ related jobs" or "good jobs for ___Category___" or "jobs in the __Category__ industry" For example "jobs in the music production industry" pulls up a number of websites with excellent suggestions for specific jobs. These are some of the search terms that work well. You can also feel free to try different terms.

Option 2: Type in your top keywords in the search bar of these free online resources and see what you find:

www.indeed.com   www.onetonline.org   www.careerbuilder.com

Write down *job titles* that you find interesting through your reseach:

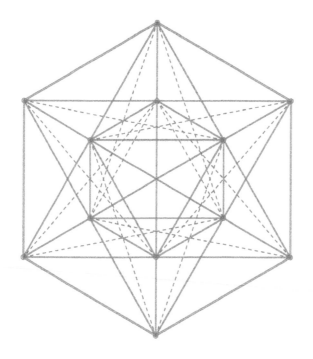

NARROWING IT DOWN

What you are doing is narrowing down the possibilities. You're constantly fine-tuning the picture. As you do more and more it becomes clearer and clearer.

- Blair Rudes

MAKING A CHOICE

You may find that there are many different options that lead to a fulfilling career and life. Thus far you've learned about parts of yourself that tend to be fairly stable, like the roots of a tree. The various job possibilities are like the branches of the tree. This next section will help you identify the strongest branch with the most foliage for this season of your life, by pin-pointing a specific job.

A lot of people get stuck at the crossroads of choice. They see a number of possibilities and have a hard time choosing which one to move forward with. Narrowing your choices down is incredibly important. If you have too many choices it can become paralyzing. In this next section you will explore what all your potential job opportunities look like and you will be guided to make the best possible choice.

Nothing is set in stone and you can always revise your life plan. In fact regular reflection is encouraged - with the clause that regular reflection does come about only when things are difficult, because no matter the choice there will be difficulties. Life is uncertain and dispositions are guaranteed to change. For some of us the most important step is just taking the first step forward towards a goal. To better understand when to keep going and when it's time to move on, please visit the Perseverance section in this guidebook for tips.

FULL POTENTIAL

CONSIDERATIONS WHILE EXPLORING JOBS

80,000 Hours, a research organization based out of England, reviewed two decades of work and over 60 studies finding there are six key ingredients of what makes for a dream job:[1]

1. Work that is engaging

2. Work that helps others

3. Work you're good at

4. Work with supportive colleagues

5. Lack of major stressors, such as a far commute, long hours, unfair pay, and job insecurity

6. Work that fits with the rest of your life

Other factors to keep in mind while going through this section:

- Growth and decline trajectories within industries (including the future impact of automation)
- Educational requirements
- Skills needed
- Time and money investment to gain required skills/education
- Daily tasks
- Earning potentials
- Ladder progression opportunities
- Location of jobs (which city has the best jobs for this field and what jobs are available in your local area)
- The impact on your lifestyle and personal life

JOBS OF INTEREST

Let's start by writing down all the jobs you find of interest. This can include jobs you've found interesting in the past, and jobs you have found through using this guidebook Don't worry if you have more or less than the indicated slots below - if you have more, just write them below the allocated slots:

1. ....
2. ....
3. ....
4. ....
5. ....
6. ....
7. ....
8. ....
9. ....
10. ....
11. ....
12. ....
13. ....

14. ....
15. ....
16. ....
17. ....
18. ....
19. ....
20. ....
21. ....
22. ....
23. ....
24. ....
25. ....
26. ....

Are any of the jobs better placed as a hobby or something you want to do in your spare time?

Possible Hobbies:

1. ....
2. ....
3. ....

FULL POTENTIAL

TOP FIVE JOBS

Next, you want to pick your top five job interests. A trick that works well is to look at two jobs side by side and ask yourself, "If I had to pick only one, which one would it be?" Take into consideration whether or not the job logically fits well for you and your lifestyle (see the list of considerations - back two pages). With this kind of process people tend to predominantly use the mind and set aside emotions and/or intuition. Factor in how you emotionally or intuitively feel about the jobs that you are considering. If you ignore your intuition you may be over rationalizing your choices. When you ignore your intuition you are unable to properly feel out the situation and assess the wisest direction to take.

You can use the following exercise to help you determine if a job feels right for you. Close your eyes and think about all aspects of the job and how it would personally impact you: What will you be doing all day? Who will you be interacting with? How will work influence your personal life?, etc. After you have spent time imagining your life with that job, check in to see how you are feeling. Some clues related to how you feel might be if you are energized or tired or are excited or neutral. Do you need more guidance on how to identify if something feels right? Flip through this guidebook to the Perseverance section for tips.

Keep going until you have arrived at the top five jobs you would like to explore. If you feel uncertain about cutting out some of the jobs and it exceeds the top five, please also list them. We don't want to cut out a job that could still be a good fit. List the jobs below:

Possible Jobs:

1.
2.
3.
4.
5.

SHARE YOUR IDEAS!

Share your list of top possible jobs with people that you trust. This is a great way to further think about alternatives and receive feedback. Speaking with others helps you to hash out your ideas, but be careful not to let people's views limit you. Sometimes people have a hard time seeing your vision. Jack Ma, founder of Alibaba and now one of the richest people in China, was told Alibaba was not a good idea by multiple people. If Jack listened to them he would not be a billionaire and might still be struggling to survive. Trust yourself through this process. Some questions you can ask:

- Do you think these jobs would be a good fit for me? If yes, why?
- Are there any reasons you think I would not like any of these jobs?
- What job do you think would fit me the best?
- Is there anything else you would like to share?

Use below for notes from your discussions:

FULL POTENTIAL

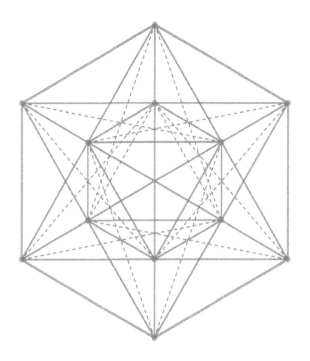

RESEARCHING
POTENTIAL JOBS

Research is formalized curiosity. It is poking and prying with a purpose.

- Zora Neale Hurston

RESEARCHING JOBS

We are now going to move from ideation into action by doing some really practical research about the career paths you're considering. Websites to help you with your research are:

www.glassdoor.com   **www.indeed.com**   **www.onetonline.org**

Write down the following for your jobs of interest:

*Example of steps, time, and money for becoming a web designer:

Three-month online course (costing $5,000) + six months of volunteering to gain experience and build a portfolio + three months for job searching = $5,000 and an estimated twelve months before obtaining a job (feel free to also include money lost because of time investment).

JOB 1

Job title:.. Average salary:...................................

Job description:...
....
....
....
....

Daily tasks:...
....
....

Working environment:...
....

Colleagues you interact with:..
....

FULL POTENTIAL

What steps, time and money would you need to get this position:

How would you feel working in this position (be as descriptive as possible):

JOB 2

Job title: _____ Average salary: _____

Job description: _____

Daily tasks: _____

Working environment: _____

Colleagues you interact with:

What steps, time and money would you need to get this position:

How would you feel working in this position (be as descriptive as possible):

JOB 3

Job title: Average salary:

Job description:

Daily tasks:

FULL POTENTIAL

Working environment:

Colleagues you interact with:

What steps, time and money would you need to get this position:

How would you feel working in this position (be as descriptive as possible):

JOB 4

Job title: .... Average salary:

Job description:

Daily tasks:

Working environment:

Colleagues you interact with:

What steps, time and money would you need to get this position:

How would you feel working in this position (be as descriptive as possible):

JOB 5

Job title: Average salary:

Job description:

FULL POTENTIAL

Job description cont.:

Daily tasks:

Working environment:

Colleagues you interact with:

What steps, time and money would you need to get this position:

How would you feel working in this position (be as descriptive as possible):

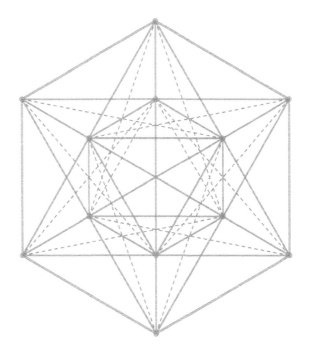

(IN)FORMATIONAL
INTERVIEWS

The art and science of asking questions is the source of all knowledge.

- Thomas Berger

UNDERSTANDING JOBS

Informational interviews can provide intimate knowledge about a job that you can't find through online searches. Learning from others can help you determine if a job is a good fit for you. You can also gain insight into the steps needed to obtain the position of interest based on the interviewee's path and you may even be able to bypass potential mistakes. The more people you can talk to the better. Everyone has a different experience and unique information to share. With your informational interviews make sure you are asking questions versus talking about yourself.

For lots of people this can be intimidating. If you have inhibitions about doing this please skip forward to the tips and tricks, networking section in this guidebook. There are tremendous benefits to informational interviews. Some of the benefits are:

- Interviews are a risk-free way to explore careers without investing a lot of time and energy.
- Learn from others' personal experiences to optimize and expedite obtaining your desired job position.
- Get first-hand relevant information that can only be obtained through conversations.
- Expand your network.
- Find a potential mentor or sponsor.
- Get your foot in the door.
  *Getting your foot in the door may result from an informational interview, but it is not something you should expect. Recommending you for a position reflects on the person who is referring you, so it is a lot to ask of a stranger. Please do not treat informational interviews as ways to get hired. The interview may evolve into a referral for a position, but rather than expecting this to happen, allow it to unfold naturally. Taking this approach will be much more comfortable for both you and the person you are speaking with.

Read through the full (In)formational Interviews section before proceeding with contacting people.

RESEARCHING PEOPLE

You will be provided with tools for outreach. Feel free to use these tools or reach out in a manner that feels right for you.

Warning - Vekita and Full Potential takes no responsibility for interactions. Please be cautious. You can choose not to do this if you do not feel comfortable.

Tips for staying safe:

- Go to reputable websites for business contact information only (Linkedin, Yelp, etc.).
- Be careful with how much information you provide and don't share highly personal information.
- Schedule phone calls and if you do decide to meet in person, meet in a public place and practice caution.

Where to search for people:

- LinkedIn.com (good for finding specific people)
- Yelp.com (good for exploring smaller businesses and finding specific people)
- Google.com (good for general searches)

Research at least five people who have your ideal job. You will be contacting them to ask if they would be willing to do an informal interview. If you have the time and feel comfortable, contact more people. You may find that people are slow to email you back and phone calls are more efficient. The more people you contact, the more likely you can complete your informational interviews in a timely manner. You may want to move forward with other activities in this guidebook, while you wait to schedule and conduct your informational interviews.

Professional #1:

Name:

Company / Organization:

Position:

Contact information (Email, LinkedIn Profile, Website, Phone Number, etc.):

FULL POTENTIAL

What stood out to you about this person:

_____

_____

Professional #2:

Name:_____

Company / Organization:_____

Position:_____

Contact information (Email, LinkedIn Profile, Website, Phone Number, etc.):

_____

What stood out to you about this person:

_____

_____

Professional #3:

Name:_____

Company / Organization:_____

Position:_____

Contact information (Email, LinkedIn Profile, Website, Phone Number, etc.):

_____

What stood out to you about this person:

_____

_____

VEKITA

Professional #4:

Name:...

Company / Organization:..

Position:..

Contact information (Email, LinkedIn Profile, Website, Phone Number, etc.):

....

What stood out to you about this person:

....

....

Professional #5:

Name:...

Company / Organization:..

Position:..

Contact information (Email, LinkedIn Profile, Website, Phone Number, etc.):

....

What stood out to you about this person:

....

....

FULL POTENTIAL

INTERVIEW QUESTIONS

Pick **three** of the questions below and write **two** personalized questions for each person you will be interviewing. Have an additional **two** extra questions in mind to ask in case you have additional time. So you will have a total of seven questions prepared before your interview.

- How did you decide on this field of work and what steps did you take to obtain your current position?
- What do you like best and least about your work?
- What is a typical day or week like for someone in your profession?
- If you could go back in time and give yourself career advice, what would it be?
- What have been your biggest challenges within your career?
- How does this job impact your personal life?
- What current issues and trends in the field should I be aware of?
- Who are some of the people in your industry that you admire and why?
- How do you see your career changing in the next 10-20 years?
- What related fields do you think I should consider looking into?
- What skills and attributes are essential tosucceed in your job/field?
- What steps would you recommend I take to prepare to enter this field? And what are common entry-level jobs?
- What are some creative ways people in your industry have earned a living? (Good question if you're interested in arts or sports)
- Can you suggest anyone else I could contact for additional information?
- Do you have any recommendations for learning resources for industry trends or industry tips, such as books, blogs, podcasts, etc.?

Write two unique questions related to the research you did on the individual you want to interview.

Personalized questions for interview #1:

1.

2.

Personalized questions for interview #2:

1.

2.

Personalized questions for interview #3:

1.

2.

Personalized questions for interview #4:

1.

2.

Personalized questions for interview #5:

1. ....

   ....

2. ....

   ....

SAMPLE CALL SCRIPT

My name is _____ and I am currently exploring possible careers that would fit well with my attributes and interests. Through my research I identified _____ (name of job) as one of my top five potential jobs. I was wondering if you would be open to sharing with me more about the industry and your personal experience. Do you have 15 minutes for an informational phone interview to help me get a realistic idea of what it means to work in your profession? If you don't have time now, we can schedule a time that is convenient for you.

EMAIL TEMPLATE

Hello/Dear (person's name),

My name is _____ and I am currently exploring possible careers that would fit well with my attributes and interests. Through my research I identified _____ (name of job) as one of my top five potential jobs. While researching careers I came acr oss your profile/website, and _____ (say what stood out for you here about this person/business) caught my attention. Do you have 15 minutes for an informational phone interview to help me get a realistic idea of what it means to work in your profession? If you are available, please let me know a few days and times that work for you to speak. Thank you for your consideration and I look forward to hearing back from you.

Best,   (your name)

INTERVIEW NOTES

Interview #1

Question #1

Notes:

Question #2

Notes:

Question #3

Notes:

Question #4

Notes:

FULL POTENTIAL

Interview #2

Question #1

Notes:

Question #2

Notes:

Question #3

Notes:

Question #4

Notes:

Interview #3

Question #1

Notes:

Question #2

Notes:

Question #3

Notes:

Question #4

Notes:

FULL POTENTIAL

Interview #4

Question #1

Notes:

Question #2

Notes:

Question #3

Notes:

Question #4

Notes:

Interview #5

Question #1

Notes:

Question #2

Notes:

Question #3

Notes:

Question #4

Notes:

FULL POTENTIAL

ADDITIONAL NOTES

INTERNSHIPS AND JOB SHADOWING

Experiencing or observing a job you're interested in is a powerful way to know if the job is right for you. If you can spend time in the workplace, that is highly advised. You can also volunteer with nonprofits that may need help in the field you want to explore. Due to potential logistical constraints and timing, this step is not required for this guidebook, but highly recommended.

YOUR IDEAL JOB

Now that you have explored your top five jobs, it is time to pick just one to focus on. This can be intimidating, or maybe it is exhilarating. This does not have to be a forever commitment, but do commit to this job for at least two years. The first year is always a learning curve and time of adjustment. Year two is when you start to become more comfortable and get a true sense of whether or not it is the right job for you. If you still feel stuck, try doing the practice below for each job that you are still considering:

1. Choose a job to focus on for the day. Guide your thoughts to think about, "What would my life look like if I had this job?"

2. Start your day by waking up and writing down your thoughts about how you would imagine your life would look if you had this career. Write down anything that may be important to you or that you are curious about regarding the job or what life might look like with this job.

- What would be your daily activities?

- What does this life look like if you started the job tomorrow?

- What does life look like if you stayed with the job five years down-the-line? What does life look like ten years down-the-line?

- How could this job impact your family or long-term goals?

- Think about your future self and your goals, such as starting a family or being able to travel or buy a house, etc. Does this job match those goals?

FULL POTENTIAL

- Relationships are an important factor for happiness: this could mean friends, family or romantic partnerships. Think about how this job would impact your relationships.

3. Spend the day focusing on this career.

- Bring your attention to your daily activities and notice if anything would shift if you were to have this job.

- Play with imagining what life would be like if you had this job throughout the day.

- Ask people you encounter throughout the day if they know of anyone that has that job, what their thoughts are about the job, or any other questions that you may be looking for more information about with the job.

4. At the end of the day, journal the same question you started out with (without looking at what you wrote previously). What would my life look like if I had this job?

5. Next, don't do anything. Let it be.

6. Take a break for a whole day before doing the same with the next job you are interested in.

7. Repeat this until you have gone through all the potential jobs you were interested in. After you have gone through all the potential jobs, look back at your notes and choose the job you feel the most interested in.

THE JOB I WILL BE FOCUSING ON IS:

....

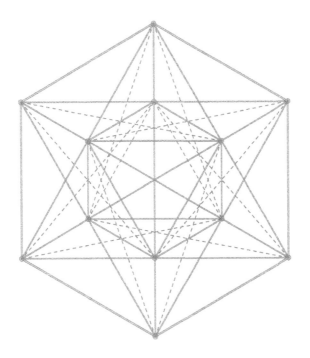

COMPANY CULTURE

Company culture is the personality of the organization. It is the company's shared beliefs, values and practices. The culture guides how employees think, act, interact, and feel. Identifying the most ideal culture to work for can be just as important as identifying the specific job you want to pursue. The best company culture fit is one that feels like there are the least restrictions because the way the organization operates matches the way you prefer to work.

- Nicole Serena Silver

DESIGNING YOUR COMPANY CULTURE

For this next exercise, you will develop your ideal company culture. By developing your own company culture you will be able to identify what is important to you and apply this knowledge to your job search. **The type of company is not important**. What is important is learning the different aspects of culture and your preferences.

Vision: A vision is a short statement that guides the company's purpose by capturing the company's core mission. Example: Instagram's vision statement is, "To capture and share the world's moments."

Write your company's vision statement in two sentences or less.

Narrative: The narrative is the story behind an organization's creation, history, and existence. Example: Instagram was created in San Francisco by Kevin Systrom and Mike Krieger in 2010 as a free mobile app. Two years later they had over 100 million active users. Instagram was acquired by Facebook with a team of thirteen employees for approximately one billion dollars.

Describe your company's story (creation, history, first employees, etc.)

Values: Values are a set of guidelines of the behaviors and mindsets needed to achieve the company's vision. Example: Giving back, move fast, be bold, and add value to people's social lives.

List three values for your company.

1. ....

2. ....

3. ....

Practices: Practices are the actions that support your company values. It is how things get done and how people interact with each other. Whatever an organization's values, they must be reinforced daily within the workplace. Example: Giving back = have a day quarterly where employees volunteer.

Give each value from above an actionable practice.

1. .... = ...

   ....

   ....

   ....

2. .... = ...

   ....

   ....

   ....

3. .... = ...

   ....

   ....

FULL POTENTIAL

People: People drive culture. It is in the company's best interest to find people that match its culture in order to be effective. Example: What are some ways to increase our products impact on peoples social lives?

Write three questions to help you identify if someone is a good fit for your company culture.

1.

2.

3.

Place: The location, building design and interior styling impact the values and behaviors of people in a workplace. **Sketch a work environment that reflects your company culture. You can choose to sketch the interior or exterior of your building.**

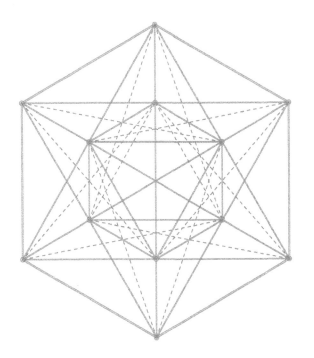

FINDING YOUR
IDEAL COMPANY

*If you get the culture right,
most of the other stuff will
just take care of itself.*

- Tony Hsieh

COMPANY SIZE

Identifying what is your ideal company size and stage of growth will help you zero in on the best kind of company to work for. Please check ONLY the boxes that you feel strongly about. For some people, you may find that pros fall into cons and cons fall into pros. For example, large businesses have more procedures - which is listed as a con - but may be a pro if you like a structured work environment. If you feel strongly that a con falls in the opposite category for you, go ahead and check that box.

Small - 0-99 Employees

Pros:

- ☐ More of an intimate and family feel.
- ☐ More opportunities for leadership positions.
- ☐ Less bureaucracy and less complexity.
- ☐ You will know everyone from the receptionist all the way up to the boss.
- ☐ You usually have to help with a number of job functions, which allows for you to gain a wider exposure to different job positions.
- ☐ Typically there are less rules and more flexibility.
- ☐ Chances are much higher that you can effect change on the company and greater opportunity to have more influence.
- ☐ The company is more agile and can adapt quickly.
- ☐ Less hierarchical.
- ☐ Your success is visible.
- ☐ Gain experience inorder to get hired into a bigger company.

Cons:

- ☐ Salaries may be lower.
- ☐ Professional development opportunities such as reimbursement for certification fees and professional memberships are less likely to be available.
- ☐ There may not be a lot of people with specific expertise to learn from.
- ☐ Your failures are more visible.
- ☐ Technology offerings may be limited.

- [ ] You may have to work longer hours and support colleagues to avoid short-staffing or immediate project needs.
- [ ] Typically one location vs large or medium that may have multiple locations. Multiple locations can allow for learning from diverse geographic influences and can be a plus if you are wanting to work from numerous locations or would like the option to transfer to a different state or even country.
- [ ] There are fewer formal training programs, and benefits packages can be more limited.
- [ ] Opportunities to transfer to other departments may be limited or non-existent.

Medium - 100-999 **Employees**

If you feel stuck between small and large companies, a mid-sized company may be a good place for you. Medium companies are a blend of small and large companies. If you decide to move forward with looking for a medium-sized company you may want to ask questions around the qualities you liked or did not like of both small and large companies when determining if the company will be the right fit for you.

Pros:
- [ ] Usually have updated technology and accounting systems.
- [ ] Good for lateral career moves.
- [ ] You may still know most people in the company, but have a bit more autonomy.
- [ ] The chain of command is shorter.
- [ ] There is someone to back you up for vacation or sick days.

Cons:
- [ ] Won't be able to compete with the salaries, benefits or prestige of a bigger company.
- [ ] Not as much influence as a smaller company.

FULL POTENTIAL

Large - 999+ **Employees**

Pros:

- ☐ Recognizable name for your resume.
- ☐ If you want to move to a new city, you can most likely stay at your job and transfer.
- ☐ You can switch jobs without leaving.
- ☐ Large companies are typically international.
- ☐ Usually have competitive salaries and good benefits packages.
- ☐ Lots of specialists that can help support your work projects and that you can learn from to enhance your own knowledge and skill base.
- ☐ More perks, such as company happy hours, special events, food, daycare, gym, etc.
- ☐ You will be in a more specialized role and be able to fully develop a specific expertise or job function.
- ☐ Large companies typically have a structure in place to move up the career ladder.
- ☐ Everything is at scale with enterprises.

Cons:

- ☐ More structure and procedures.
- ☐ Change happens slowly.
- ☐ You may have to get approval from several levels of management before implementing new processes.
- ☐ You will likely only get to know the people you work with day in and day out and you won't get to know the other employees of the company.
- ☐ Enterprises have established processes, regulations, and protocols that you need to comply with and follow - which may interfere with pushing your work forward and can be complex to navigate.
- ☐ Can be impersonal and easier to get lost in the shuffle.
- ☐ More coworkers will be competing with you for promotions.

STARTUP VS MATURE COMPANY

Small and mid-sized companies could be just starting up or are established and have been operating for a long period of time, whereas large sized companies typically are solidly established. Figuring out if you would prefer to work for a startup or an established company is an important factor to finding the ideal company you want to work for.

Startup companies

Pros:

- ☐ Potential for a small business to become a big business which can offer the financial benefits of being there in the early stages.
- ☐ Gain multiple skills and good if you enjoy learning on the job in a fast pace environment.
- ☐ You can be much more innovative.
- ☐ Usually work without supervision.
- ☐ Easier to get your foot in the door to get hired, especially for people who are wanting to transition careers.
- ☐ Energetic and dynamic environment.
- ☐ More flexibility and freedom.

Cons:

- ☐ Heavy workload and long hours.
- ☐ High pressure and stressful.
- ☐ Lack of job stability/security.
- ☐ Low pay initially.
- ☐ Startups have a small workforce with a big mission, every single person factors into its success. It's not as viable to take a sick or personal day.
- ☐ You may work long hours and not have much of a work-life balance.
- ☐ May be unorganized or lacks structure.
- ☐ Managers are typically less experienced.
- ☐ The company may hire friends versus experienced professionals.
- ☐ Startups are often chaotic and unstructured. They're still molding, adjusting the product-market fit, and learning how to run a business.

FULL POTENTIAL

Established Company

Pros:

- ☐ Likely has a strong and experienced leadership team.
- ☐ Clear about long-term strategy.
- ☐ More stable.
- ☐ Established brand and customers.
- ☐ Learned from successes and failures.
- ☐ More structured guidance and time to acclimate to systems.

Cons:

- ☐ The company may be stuck in their ways.
- ☐ Your impact won't be as significant as at a startup.
- ☐ May not be as exciting.
- ☐ You will have to navigate the bureaucracies, and will be more constrained to follow a specific protocol.

WHAT KIND OF COMPANY WOULD YOU LIKE TO WORK AT?

- ☐ Small Company
- ☐ Mid-sized Company
- ☐ Large Company

I would prefer to work for a:

- ☐ Startup Company
- ☐ Established Company

The top characteristics of the company I want to work for are:

HOW TO LOOK FOR COMPANY CULTURE

Now that you know what your ideal job and company size is, it's time to figure out what would be your most favorable companies to work for. The Company Culture and Values activities you did in this guidebook are good resources to help you find businesses that are a good fit. Research companies in your area. If you are willing to relocate you can broaden your search. Below are tips that can assist you with identifying company culture.

Characteristics to look for in the workplace:
- Interactions between co-workers and managers.
- How decisions are made.
- Communication style with team members, management, and across departments.
- Office layouts are indicators of how employees may interact.
- Other things to consider: the attire employees wear to work, what are the breakrooms like, what kinds of benefits are offered to employees and any events companies host.

Looking online:
- Explore the characteristics of a company's website, social media and advertising. The images and wording used can tell a lot about a company. See if the website has the company's mission, vision and values listed.
- A great resource to look up employee reviews and company culture assessments is **glassdoor.com**. Keep in mind that change is possible within a company, especially when directors or managers are replaced, which can shift the culture.
- Look at websites where companies are reviewed by customers to see what the customers' experiences has been. If it is a smaller business, **Yelp.com** may be a good resource.

Ask people who have worked at the company about their experience:
- To get the most up-to-date information, ask questions related to what you are looking for in informational interviews. Check on LinkedIn for people who have previously worked at companies you are interested in. You may want to consider contacting people who are no longer working there, because they typically have more freedom to answer your questions honestly without putting their job at risk.
- Ask questions during your interview. Most HR managers appreciate curiosity around the role and company, but always be conscious of how you phrase your questions. Suggested questions are included in the Getting Hired section of tips and tricks in this guidebook.

FULL POTENTIAL

YOUR IDEAL COMPANY

Use the previous page to help find companies that you would like to work for and write in your top choices below.

Company 1..

Company 2..

Company 3..

Company 4..

Company 5..

TEAM CULTURE

Each department and team within a company will have a different personality. For example, the personalities of the sales team are most likely going to be vastly different than the personalities of the programming team. Every team will have its distinct nuances, so make sure when interviewing to ask about the dynamics of the specific teams as well as the company. Team culture can influence your experience just as much as company culture. Teams will have their own unique culture, but company culture will always influence teams. Let's use the analogy of the United States representing company culture and a state representing departments or teams. California will be different from Texas, but both will have the overarching influence of the United States culture.

YOUR IDEAL JOB AND COMPANY

You have been gifted this life, and my hope is for you to live it to the fullest. Nelson Mandela said it best, "There is no passion to be found playing small - in settling for a life that is less than the one you are capable of living." Give yourself the gift of setting powerful intentions for yourself. You have come a long way on your journey and worked hard to get to this point. What have you identified as your ideal job and company?

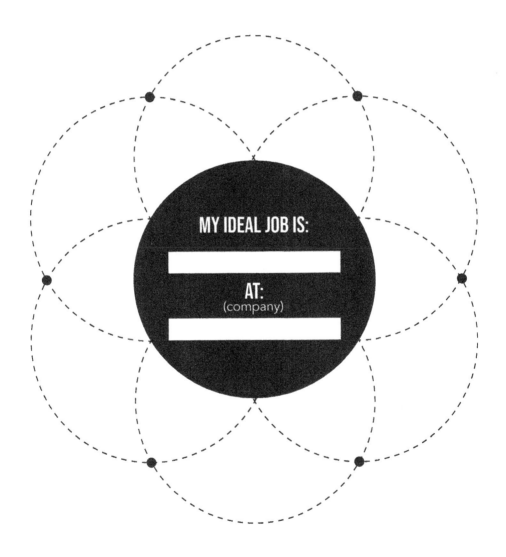

MY IDEAL JOB IS:

AT:
(company)

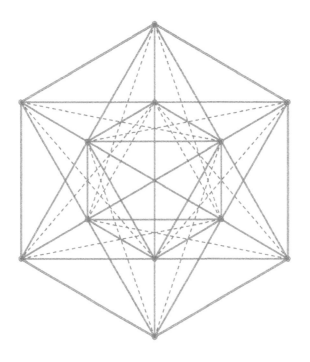

PLAN FOR ACHIEVING YOUR GOAL

If the plan doesn't work, change the plan, but never the goal.

- Unknown

MAKING A PLAN

Now let's make a plan for your success. You are about to draw a map that will identify the steps needed to obtain your ideal job. Before you draw out the map, use a blank piece of paper to see if you can find multiple ways to achieve your career goal. Here is an example of the different paths you can take to become a video game designer:

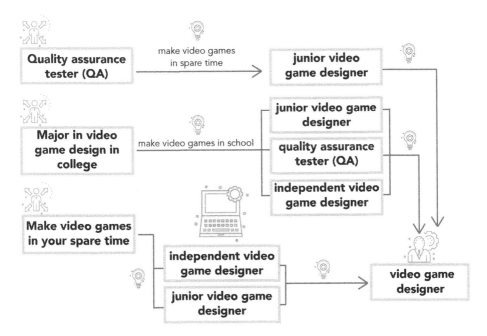

If you are not sure about the steps, you can:

- Look on LinkedIn to see people's backgrounds with the job you desire. You can review the steps they list in their profile that got them into their current position.
- Type into a search engine: steps needed to become _____ (job title).
- Gladeo.org has job mapping flow charts under the "Landing The Job" tab.
- Conduct more informational interviews. This is the most powerful source for understanding the details of job paths.
- Find a mentor or ask someone for assistance (Vekita Career Coaches are available for hire at **www.vekitapd.com**).

HOW JOB PATHS MAY DIFFER

Understanding the different ways to reach your ideal job will help you choose the most congruent path. When you are choosing you may want to consider:

- What is the time and money commitment?

- Is school or training needed? What is the timeline for admittance and how hard is it to get into a program?

- How will the different paths will impact your personal life?

- What is the more appealing path, that can help you get your foot in the door easier, with future employers or your current employer if you are wanting to change your role within the company?

- How does each path impact job flexibility for potential career pivots?

Here are a few more examples of how paths can differ:

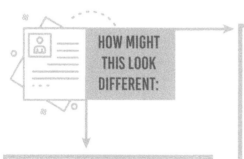

HOW MIGHT THIS LOOK DIFFERENT:

TEACHER:
Obtain a part time job to help pay for college → attend two year college and obtain an Associate's Degree → transfer to four year university → complete last two years of major for degree → public school teacher

TEACHER:
Attend four year university → volunteer or intern with a teaching position → become a substitute teacher → public school teacher

SOFTWARE ENGINEER:
Attend a coding bootcamp → build your portfolio → internship → continue to grow skillset → software engineer

SOFTWARE ENGINEER:
Attend four year university → build portfolio → software engineer

GRAPHIC DESIGNER:
Take InDesign and Photoshop classes at a community college → volunteer → build portfolio → become a freelance graphic designer

GRAPHIC DESIGNER:
Attend an art school → build your portfolio → graphic designer

CAREER ROADMAP

Now is the time to turn your dream into a reality by creating a personalized roadmap to reach your career aspirations. Your roadmap will act as a guide, starting where you are today and plotting the path to achieving your goal. Write in each step necessary to obtain your goal in the hexagons. You do not have to fill in ALL the hexagons on the goals map and if you have more steps than what are on the map, you can draw them into the blank areas on the exterior of the roadmap.

You will find circles on either side of the map where you can write in the core aspects of what you've discovered about yourself through this guidebook. The circles act as a reminder of what's important to you to help guide you to act in alignment along your journey.

You may want to add or remove steps as you progress along the way. This is a living document that you can always update or change. Please make this map your own. There are no rules, only guidance and suggestions. Feel free to design your map by collaging, coloring or anything else you'd like to do to personalize it.

On the page after next, you will fill out your roadmap. You can also download a copy and place it somewhere that you will see it often to help remind you of what your current steps are and what are the next steps to come. Download the roadmap at: **vekitapd.com/resources**

Want a different style of map? We will be periodically adding new maps designed by different artists on our website. Want to submit your art to be considered for others to use? Email: **info@vekitapd.com**

Your roadmap is a blueprint to help you plan out all the steps necessary to achieve your goal. It is important to maintain a balance of planning and receptivity of going with the flow. Life is not always a straight line. You may find twists and turns along your path. Sometimes the twists and turns take you to unexpected places which end up leading you to exactly where you want to be. I highly encourage you to commit to a two-year plan, but the most important thing is to listen to yourself and be aware of what will best serve you. Being open and listening to life's cues paired with action and a plan is the optimum way to be able to achieve your goals. If you are ever unsure of what to do you can visit the Perseverance section of this guidebook.

FULL POTENTIAL

EXAMPLE

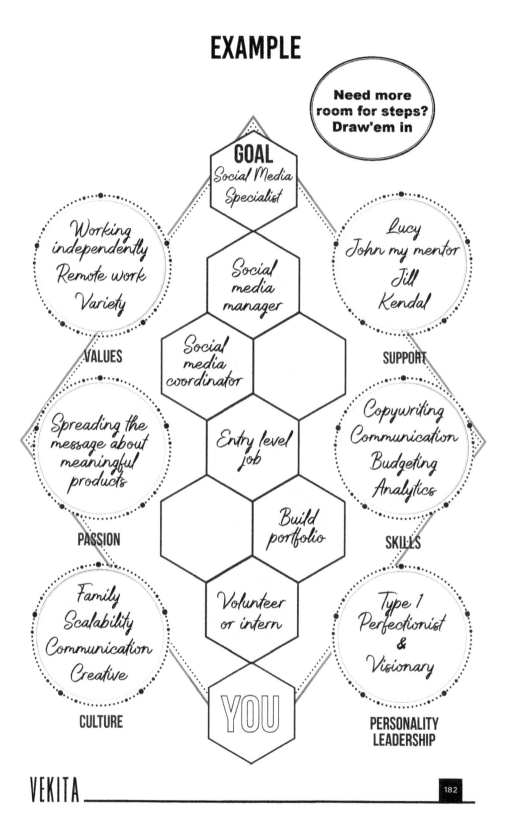

Need more room for steps? Draw 'em in

GOAL
Social Media Specialist

Social media manager

Social media coordinator

Entry level job

Build portfolio

Volunteer or intern

YOU

Working independently
Remote work
Variety

VALUES

Lucy
John my mentor
Jill
Kendal

SUPPORT

Spreading the message about meaningful products

PASSION

Copywriting
Communication
Budgeting
Analytics

SKILLS

Family
Scalability
Communication
Creative

CULTURE

Type 1
Perfectionist
&
Visionary

PERSONALITY LEADERSHIP

YOUR GOALS ROADMAP

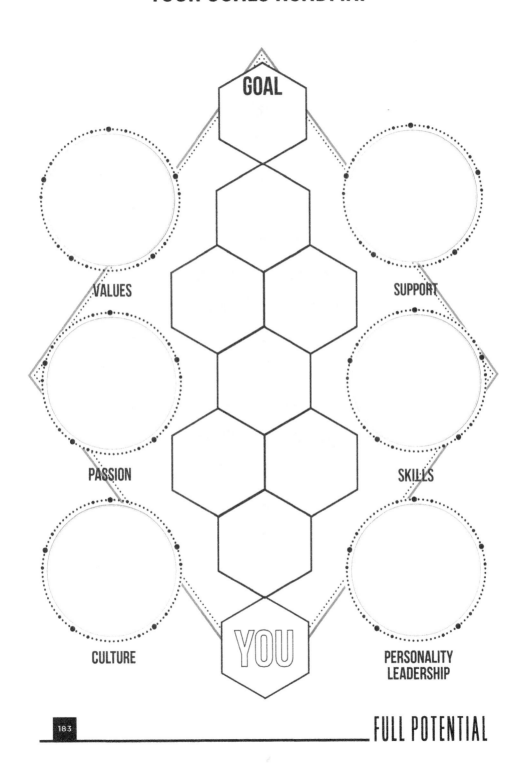

SUBGOAL MAP

On your Goal Roadmap you created steps to reach your goal. Each step is represented by a hexagon. Every identified step/hexagon is a subgoal that has its own set of tasks to help you reach your main goal. A Subgoal Map is the breakdown of what is needed just for one step alone. Please create a Subgoal Map for the first step on your Goal Roadmap. After you have accomplished your first step, create a Subgoal Map for the next step on your Goal Roadmap.

Download and print the Subgoal Map at **vekitapd.com/resources**. Hang your subgoal steps in a place where you can view it frequently to keep you

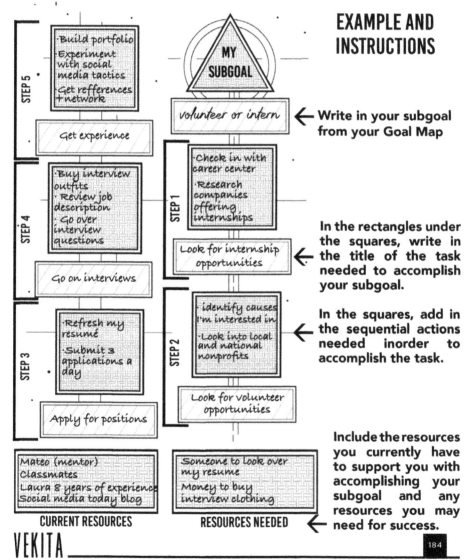

EXAMPLE AND INSTRUCTIONS

STEP 5
- Build portfolio
- Experiment with social media tactics
- Get refferences + network

Get experience

MY SUBGOAL

volunteer or intern ← **Write in your subgoal from your Goal Map**

STEP 1
- Check in with career center
- Research companies offering internships

Look for internship opportunities ← **In the rectangles under the squares, write in the title of the task needed to accomplish your subgoal.**

STEP 4
- Buy interview outfits
- Review job description
- Go over interview questions

Go on interviews

STEP 2
- Identify causes I'm interested in
- Look into local and national nonprofits ← **In the squares, add in the sequential actions needed inorder to accomplish the task.**

STEP 3
- Refresh my resumé
- Submit 3 applications a day

Apply for positions

Look for volunteer opportunities

CURRENT RESOURCES
- Mateo (mentor)
- Classmates
- Laura 8 years of experience
- Social media today blog

RESOURCES NEEDED
- Someone to look over my resume
- Money to buy interview clothing

← **Include the resources you currently have to support you with accomplishing your subgoal and any resources you may need for success.**

VEKITA

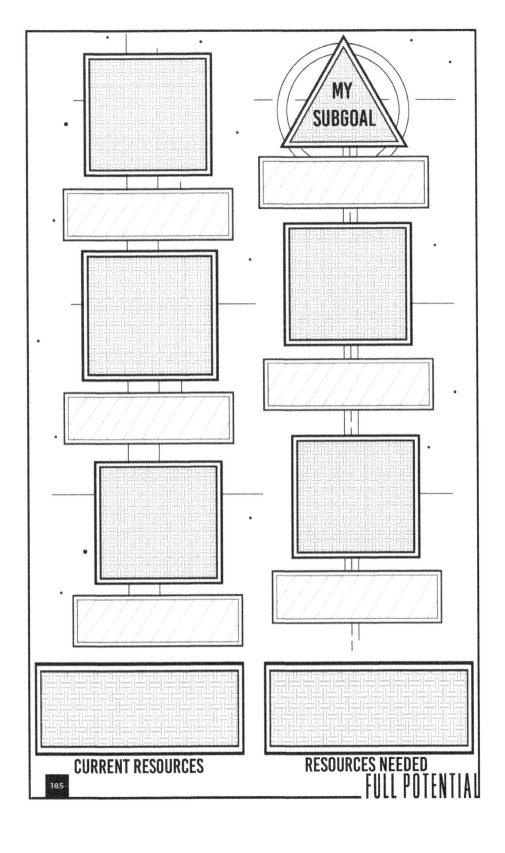

MY
SUBGOAL

CURRENT RESOURCES

RESOURCES NEEDED

FULL POTENTIAL

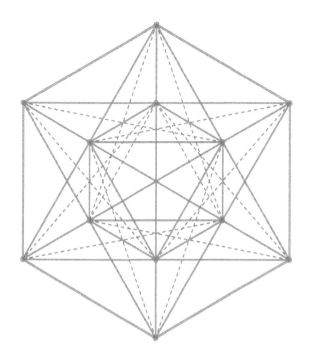

PUTTING YOUR PLAN INTO ACTION

Knowledge is of no value unless you put it into practice.

- Anton Chekhov

SET SMART GOALS

WOW, you did it! You worked hard and your work will pay off. Congratulations. For your final wrap up, let's do some planning to strategicly strengthen your opportunity for succcess by using the SMART formula. The method is easy to follow and provides powerful results. SMART stands for:

SPECIFIC — you know what you want to achieve.
Example: Get into law school.

MEASURABLE — you know how to gain evidence to measure your progress.
Example: How many law schools you apply to.

ATTAINABLE — you can obtain the necessary skills and resources to be able to accomplish your goal within a certain timeframe.
Example: You can sign up for the Law School Admission Test before your application due date and that you have the time to do a prep course.

RELEVANT — make sure your goal aligns with your broader objectives.
Example: Become an estate planning lawyer.

TIME-BOUND — create a concrete timeframe for completion.
Example: Applications are due in three months.

Using the SMART method answer the following questions:

What will you be doing to reach your goal over the next month?

What will you be doing to reach your goal over the next three months?

What will you be doing to reach your goal over the next year?

FULL POTENTIAL

What will you be doing to reach your goal over the next five years?

....

....

....

If you do all the steps needed to reach your goal, what will your life look like twenty years from now?

....

....

....

SUPPORT FOR ACHIEVING YOUR GOALS

Making big changes in your life and pursuing goals can be challenging. Now that you have a plan, you can choose to do this on your own or with support. Creating a personal board of directors (PBOD) can be helpful in many ways. A PBOD is a group of people who support you, hold you accountable and can act as a sounding board. When forming your PBOD, you'll want to pick people who will be direct and truthful. You typically don't want anyone who is too closely tied to your personal life or any of your desired outcomes.

How you connect with your PBOD is up to you. You can choose to connect one on one with the different members of your board or you can form a group, where each of you support one another. You will want to decide together how often and in what form you will connect. One great way to stay connected is to share goals and daily progress on cloud-sharing platforms, such as applications like Google Drive's Excel spreadsheets.

VEKITA RESOURCES

Vekita Career and Life Coaches: **vekitapd.com**

Connect with us and others going through the same process on social media: **Facebook Groups: Vekita Full Potential - Insta: @vekitapd - LinkedIn: Vekita**

A calendar for mastering happiness and success: **thehappinessplanner.com**

VEKITA

OVERCOMING BARRIERS

What are some of the things that hold you back from accomplishing your goals? Examples: not knowing what needs to be done, needing to build skills, increasing connections, obtaining money, boosting motivation, etc.

What advice would you give a friend to overcome these barriers?

Ask someone whose advice you trust how they would overcome these barriers. What did they have to say?

List by name the people who are support systems for you. These are your people. If you ever get stuck or in need of help, contact these people:

FULL POTENTIAL

TOOLS FOR SUCCESS

The future belongs to those who believe in the beauty of their dreams.

- Eleanor Roosevelt

TOOLS FOR ACHIEVING YOUR GOALS

You set goals for yourself to upgrade your life and become a better version of yourself. Now it is time to move from figuring out what position and lifestyle would be the best fit for you and into making your dreams a reality. It will be work and with work can come hardships. Things may not go exactly as planned and that is okay. Sometimes the best things that happen to us are the most unexpected. Use your best judgement on when to be receptive to a change in plans and when to persevere to stay on track with your goal. By being flexible, trusting in the process, having patience and working hard, you will achieve success.

The final section of this guidebook provides you with tools to help you achieve your goals. These tools come from interviewing HR managers, informational interviews with professionals, extensive research, personal perspective and through the many brilliant minds that contributed to the development of curriculum for GROWmyfuture.org. I recommend reviewing all of the sections and then dive deeper into the sections that are most relevant to you.

PERSONAL BRAND

Your brand is what people say about you when you're not in the room.

- Jeff Bezos

YOUR PERSONAL BRAND

You already have a brand; you most likely just are not aware of it. Defining your brand equips you with paintbrushes and a myriad of colors to be able to paint a picture of not only who you are, but what you want to become. Your brand is how you market yourself to the world and greatly impacts how people will perceive you. This is an opportunity to use your brand more strategically as a tool to create your ideal life.

BRAND SOCIAL MEDIA CAUTION - Job recruiters are known to retract job offers if they find questionable activities online or increase the likelihood of offering you a job if you have a positive social media presence.

According to a CareerBuilder survey, 70% of employers use social media to screen candidates during the hiring process, and about 43% of employers use social media to check on current employees. Nearly half of employers from the CareerBuilder survey (47%) say that if they can't find a job candidate online, they are less likely to call that person in for an interview. Of those who decided not to hire a candidate based on their social media profiles, the reasons included:[1]

- 39% posted provocative or inappropriate photographs, videos or information.
- 38% posted pictures of them drinking or using drugs.
- 32% had posted discriminatory comments related to race, gender, or religion.
- 30% had bad-mouthed their previous company or fellow employees.
- 27% had lied about their qualifications.
- 27% had poor communication skills.
- 22% had a screen name that was unprofessional.

THE INFLUENCES OF PEOPLE ON YOUR BRAND

Who you surround yourself with influences who you are and how people perceive your personal brand. Some questions you can ask yourself:

- Does this person make me a better person?
- Do they make me feel good about myself or bring me down?
- Am I inspired by them?
- Do they represent who I want to be?

PERSONAL BRAND STATEMENT

A personal brand statement gives people a quick glance to help them understand who you are and what makes you tick. This statement expresses the core of what drives you, your expertise, and your attributes. In general, people tend to use vague language. Don't be vague with your personal brand statement. It should be concise, descriptive, bold, and catchy. For example, "I enjoy helping others" is a vague statement. "I ask acute questions to shine a light on what holds people back in life" is bold and descriptive. If you don't have much work experience, you can highlight your attributes and how they fit into your future goals.

Examples of personal brand statements:

Keywords: builder, customer-focused, creative

Personal Brand Statement: "I build products that help people live better lives. I believe customers should always come first and strive to build and continue to improve products to best serve their needs. I leverage my creativity, cross-functional business experiences, technical background and leadership skills to bring ideas to life. I have successfully applied my passion for technology and building to startups and Fortune 10 companies."

Keywords: compassion, service, writing

Personal Brand Statement: "My compassion for people led me to want to work with other like-minded individuals to solve the issues plaguing today's society. Throughout my entire life, I naturally gravitated towards creative writing. Co-workers, family members, friends and even random strangers have complimented me on my writing skills, which led me to believe that I had a gift and a gift that could be used in service of others. Through grant writing, I have an amazing opportunity to use my writing and research skills, along with my compassion for people, to help non-profits secure the funding they need to solve some of the world's biggest problems."

Your personal brand statement can be used in versatile ways, such as putting this statement on your LinkedIn profile, in a cover letter, as an elevator pitch, etc. Let's get started!

What three keywords would you use to describe yourself?

- Think about the previous sections in this guidebook and the descriptive words you have identified about yourself.
- You can also express parts of yourself that you are still developing and feel are important to how your personal brand is perceived. For example: My intrigue of insects led me to watch just about every Youtube video existing on rare insects in the Amazon jungle and I am now taking classes on entomology.
- If you are having trouble identifying your core attributes, you can ask a few people what they think are the main words they would use to describe you.

Keyword #1:

What does this mean to you?

Keyword #2:

What does this mean to you?

Keyword #3:

What does this mean to you?

FULL POTENTIAL

PERSONAL BRAND BRAINSTORM

What gives you purpose? Why do you do what you do:

....

....

....

....

What kinds of things do you do to achieve your goals (methods, processes, etc.)?

....

....

....

What are the kinds of outcomes or results you achieve?

....

....

....

Need some more inspiration? Here are some other optional questions you can ask yourself when writing your personal statement:

- What sets you apart from everyone else?
- How has your work been beneficial for the companies you have worked for?
- What do you care deeply about?
- What is one thing you would never change about yourself?
- What do you want the world to know about you? Or how does the world benefit from you?
- What are some qualities or skills you want to develop within your personal brand?

On a separate piece of paper, feel free to answer these questions and draft your personal statement before writing it on the next page.

YOUR PERSONAL BRAND STATEMENT

Write your personal brand statement below. It is okay if it's not in perfect form. You can always change it, add to it, and improve it over time.

FULL POTENTIAL

THE PEOPLE
IN YOUR LIFE

We met for a reason;
either you're a blessing
or a lesson.

- Frank Ocean

THE PEOPLE CLOSEST TO YOU

As mentioned in the previous section, people impact your brand. The people surrounding you have a significant influence on all aspects of your life, including your career success and personal well-being. If someone has a bad reputation, is negative, or sucks your energy, that will transfer over to you. Form relationships with people at work and in your personal life, who are known to be good people, have your best interests at heart, support your goals and accomplishments, and who encourage you to become the best version of yourself. Choose wisely and don't be afraid to let go of people that don't uplift you.

Fill in the sections below for three people you spend the most time with in your personal life:

PERSON 1	PERSON 2	PERSON 3
NAME: _____	NAME: _____	NAME: _____
How does this person leave you feeling?	How does this person leave you feeling?	How does this person leave you feeling?
☐ Energized and inspired ☐ Neutral ☐ Depleted/tired	☐ Energized and inspired ☐ Neutral ☐ Depleted/tired	☐ Energized and inspired ☐ Neutral ☐ Depleted/tired
Do you uplift and inspire each other?	Do you uplift and inspire each other?	Do you uplift and inspire each other?
☐ Yes ☐ No	☐ Yes ☐ No	☐ Yes ☐ No
How do you contribute to each other's lives?	How do you contribute to each other's lives?	How do you contribute to each other's lives?

FULL POTENTIAL

Fill in the sections below for three people you spend the most time with in your professional life:

PERSON 1	PERSON 2	PERSON 3
NAME:	NAME:	NAME:

How does this person leave you feeling?

PERSON 1:
- ☐ Energized and inspired
- ☐ Neutral
- ☐ Depleted/tired

PERSON 2:
- ☐ Energized and inspired
- ☐ Neutral
- ☐ Depleted/tired

PERSON 3:
- ☐ Energized and inspired
- ☐ Neutral
- ☐ Depleted/tired

Do you uplift and inspire each other?

PERSON 1:
- ☐ Yes
- ☐ No

PERSON 2:
- ☐ Yes
- ☐ No

PERSON 3:
- ☐ Yes
- ☐ No

How do you contribute to each other's lives?

Additional notes:

DEVELOPING RELATIONSHIPS

What do you consider important qualities in friendships to be?

....

....

....

....

What are important qualities in your work relationships?

....

....

....

....

What specific types of relationships would you like to develop more of in your personal and professional life?

Examples of this may be that you would like co-workers who are direct communicators or friends who are inspiring or make you laugh. Check out the Networking section in this guidebook for tips on developing new relationships.

....

....

....

....

....

FULL POTENTIAL

GETTING HIRED

I may not be there yet, but I am closer than I was yesterday.

- Unknown

TIPS ON FINDING A JOB

The following tips are insider information given by HR professionals and GROWmyfuture contributors. Search engines can provide more general help for things such as resume formatting, power words, sample cover letters, etc.

Network!

According to numerous studies, experts have found that 70-85% of people end up landing a job through their network.[2] Having a direct connection is the best way to land a job. There are lots of ways to expand your network and gain a connection to someone who would be helpful. You can gain more tips in the Networking section of this guidebook.

Alumni Associations

If you've attended college or a trade school, you can check in with their career center to see if they have an in or any leads with companies that may be hiring. You can also research fellow alumni in a similar role or at one of your ideal companies to see if they know of any positions opening up. Additionally, it can be worthwhile to check out alumni groups and events.

Internships/Volunteering

Working for free and getting experience is a great way to make connections and potentially get hired. Volunteering creates a space where you can feel comfortable coming into the position at an entry level, which can reduce anxiety and give you room to learn. This enables you to relax and gain the experience and confidence you need to be able to advance your career goals. Volunteering even a few hours can be beneficial for building your resumé. An added advantage with volunteering is that your hours can sometimes be flexible. This of course is dependent on the organization.

Go to Events

Go to industry events that are related to the job you are interested in. This could be conferences, related groups that meet, happy hours, etc.

Go Above And Beyond in Everyday Life

If you are hardworking and kind to others, people notice and may offer you an opportunity. You may also want to have ready a 30-second introduction about yourself and your goals. You never know when you will meet someone who could be influential and you want to be prepared.

FULL POTENTIAL

Build Your Credibility

- Publish smart postings in groups on LinkedIn, Facebook, Medium blogs, and/or other places where people look for specific expertise and engage in topics related to the industry you're interested in.
- Leverage social media to build your credibility and showcase your knowledge on industry topics. You can create videos on YouTube, post on Instagram, upload articles on LinkedIn, start a blog, etc. Technology can be one of your best tools to advance your career if used right. Be conscious about what you post because it will influence your brand.
- Become an expert through ongoing, active research. Be knowledgeable on general information and trends in your desired industry - read articles, listen to podcasts, join groups, follow thought leaders, etc. You can also think outside of the box by looking at how other industry trends may impact your line of work; or even gain inspiration from other industries to approach your work in an innovative way.

Other Important Information
- Be willing to submit lots of resumés before landing a job.
- Keep your options open by applying to lots of places.
- Have patience. Getting hired takes time.

RESUMÉ TIPS

Customize Your Resumé To Each Job
- Use the same words as the job posting. This is super important. The first round of resumés sometimes go through computers that check for words that match the job description.
- Recruiters tend to take an average of seven seconds to look at your resumé, so you want to show them right away what they are looking for.

Keep It To One Or Two Pages
For people with under five years of work experience, resumés should not be more than a single page. Five years or more, you still want to try to have it be one page, but a two-page resumé is also acceptable.

Add Quantifiable Results

Add facts that are measurable. For example, the amount of people you helped on a daily basis, money you saved the company, the number of people you trained, etc.

Use Power Words/Action Verbs

These are the words at the beginning of each bullet point on your resumé that describe what tasks you did, such as "increased" or "trained." You can Google "power words for resumé" to find an abundance of resources.

Get A Proofreader

Make sure you get a second pair of eyes on your resumé. You don't want to submit a resumé with mistakes. There are free resources available to help with catching errors, such as **grammarly.com** and **hemingwayapp.com.**

Add Relevant Experience

At the end of your resumé include other experiences that would make you a good candidate. For example, volunteer work, groups you've participated in, hackathons, leadership experience, certifications, different languages you speak, etc.

Keep It Simple

Do not use a bunch of fonts, and typically avoid graphics/pictures - unless you are applying for design-related work. If you are applying internationally, research the resumé format for that country - international resumés do tend to include pictures.

INTERVIEW TIPS

Be Authentic

Be yourself. Interviewers have a good sense of when someone is not being genuine, which will reflect poorly on your chances of being hired. Plus, you don't want to be employed by a company where you have to try to fit into a work environment that's not the right match.

FULL POTENTIAL

Pursue Many Opportunities

Having a number of options that you are pursuing gives you more power and confidence. If you only have a few options, you may end up feeling desperate because you are more dependent on landing that job. Hiring managers will pick up on your confidence or your desperation. Being confident can lend itself to higher chances of getting the job. Exploring lots of opportunities is also beneficial to you, because you will have more room to evaluate whether the job is truly the right fit for you.

Do Research

Research the company (history, culture, competitors, strategic goals, etc.) the job position (expectations, department goals, etc.), average salary for the position you are seeking, and see if you can find the interview questions which others have shared on places like **glassdoor.com**. In the interview, offer relevant knowledge as to why you would be a good fit for the company and team. Showing that you took the time to learn about the business demonstrates that you care about the company and the job. This will set you apart from other candidates and will make hiring managers more interested in you.

Be Early

Leave enough cushion time for unexpected events, such as traffic. Avoid showing up stressed out and frazzled, which will impact your interview. Get there early and spend time at a nearby cafe if needed.

Ask Questions

Most hiring managers like candidates who are engaged during the interview and asking questions. Learn from the person conducting the interview what they are looking for. Remember you are interviewing them to see if they are the right fit, just as much as they are interviewing you. Specific questions you can ask are listed later in this section.

Dress Appropriately

No matter what people say, looks do matter and whether the interviewer is conscious of it or not, what you wear will leave an impression. For example,

I sometimes wear glasses to meetings because glasses represent intelligence. Strangely enough I have noticed that when I do wear my glasses, I am taken more seriously. You can research the company to see what kind of attire the employees typically wear. If you feel strongly that the attire is a misalignment for you, you may want to reevaluate if that company is a good match.

Practice

Go over possible interview questions and come up with concise answers. Add into the conversation the same words that you used to customize your resumé, based on what they are looking for in their job post. The **STAR** method is a great model for answering interview questions. The method is a framework for ensuring completeness of your story, and highlighting your strengths and achievements. Here is an example:

Situation - **Provide context and background of the situation.** Such as, what company you were working for, what you were doing, etc.

> Example: "I worked for an education company where we provided online courses to students. I worked directly with the students to provide support as they completed the courses, but one of my courses had lower enrollments than usual."

Task - **Explain the task you had to complete.** Share any problems or challenges you faced.

> Example: "We had to figure out a way to get more students enrolled. We decided to create a free trial program where students could enroll early and test out the curriculum for one week without being charged."

Action - **Describe the specific action(s) you took to complete the task.** Highlight desirable traits the person interviewing you may be looking for.

> Example: "We had never done this before, so I had to research companies that have offered free trials to understand how they did it."

Results - **Share the results of your efforts.** If possible, include tangible results such as sales increases, financial savings, people trained, etc.

> Example: "I completed this project in only two months, and it led to a 25% increase in enrollments. The free trial also became a framework that was used for future courses."

FULL POTENTIAL

QUESTIONS YOU MAY BE ASKED
DURING AN INTERVIEW:

These are typical questions a hiring manager may ask you during an interview. You will also want to research specific questions that may be asked related to the job. Sometimes you can even find the exact questions they will ask on **glassdoor.com**.

- Can you tell me about yourself?
- What are some of your hobbies outside of work?
- Why do you want this position?
- Why are you leaving your job?
- How would you describe your work style?
- What isn't on your resumé that is important for me to know about you?
- What would you say is the most important skill you've learned in your current role?
- What's an area you'd like to improve on?
- What's the biggest challenge you've faced in your previous role?
- What's some feedback you've received that was difficult to hear, but ultimately has proven really valuable?
- Tell me about a time you disagreed with a decision. What did you do?
- Tell me about a challenge or conflict you've faced, and how you dealt with it.
- What do you hope to learn/gain by getting this position?
- If you got the position, when would you be available?
- What would your expected salary be for this type of position?
- What are your future goals?
- What questions can I answer for you?

QUESTIONS YOU CAN ASK:

The questions you ask during your interview are just as important as the answers you give. Job listings are sometimes recycled from when the previous employee applied and have not been updated. The role itself might have been tweaked since the last employee and you may want to inquire about this. Here is a sample list of questions that you could ask during an interview. Choose five questions that you may want to ask in an interview. Feel free to circle them on here or write them down for reference. You may want to consider having the questions noted in your phone for convenient accessibility.

- What do you enjoy most about working here?
- What types of people are successful within the company and role?
- What is the single biggest challenge the company or department is currently facing?
- What are the current focus areas for the company as a whole?
- Where is the company headed over the next five years?
- What does success look like?
- What are the preferred forms of communication?
- How is feedback given to employees?
- Can you tell me about the team I'll be working with?
- What are the current goals for the team I would be working with?
- Who would I work with most closely?
- Who would I report to directly?
- How is information documented and shared across projects and departments?
- What are my expectations for this role?
- What are success criteria within this role and what metrics or goals will my performance be evaluated against?
- What are the most important things you'd like to see someone accomplish in the first 30, 60, and 90 days on the job?
- What would you consider top accomplishments for someone in this role over the next year?

FULL POTENTIAL

FINAL QUESTIONS

In addition to the 2-5 questions you will be asking, you may want to conclude your interview with these final questions:

- What are the next steps?
- What does the onboarding process look like? How long does it take on average?
- Is there anything else I can provide you with that would be helpful?
- Can I answer any final questions for you?

WHAT TO CONSIDER BEFORE ACCEPTING AN OFFER

- Work-life balance
- Salary and compensation
- Career-growth opportunity
- Location/commute
- Company culture
- Team and working dynamics
- Role fit to your strengths and interests

STARTING SALARY AND NEGOTIATIONS

After you have enough information about the role, hop online to research what your current experience level warrants for your salary. You can use an online salary calculator, such as payscale.com or glassdoor.com. Before you are even offered the job, have in your mind what an acceptable salary would be. However, don't discuss salary in your first interview. If you are asked what you would like your starting salary to be in the first interview you can say that you would like to first learn more about the job. Your asking salary may change with new information that you find out through the interview process, such as that the role is more senior or junior or has more responsibilities than you first imagined.

Take a look at the whole package of what is being offered (starting bonus, vacation, medical, moving allowance, company perks, stock options, 401k matches, etc.). If you receive an offer that is below what you are looking for, you can and should negotiate. In fact 73 percent of employers expect candidates to negotiate during the hiring process, according to CareerBuilder.[3] Not negotiating can cost you up to one million dollars over the course of your career. You want to stay enthusiastic about the position when negotiating. Negotiations should always be treated as a collaborative effort, where both parties are winners.

You do not have to disclose what your current salary is. However, PayScale reported that "A woman who is asked about her salary history and declines to disclose earns 1.8 percent less than a woman who discloses. If a man declines to disclose, he gets paid 1.2 percent more on average.[4]" This means different genders need to take different approaches. If you are a female and don't want to share your previous salary, you may choose to bring up these statistics to let your future employer know that you would rather not disclose your salary, but that you do not want the statistics to work against you. There are many disparities not just in the workplace, but also in life. Society is shifting towards more equality, but it will take time. It starts with you: whether you are a man or a woman, we all play a role. It is not us versus them; it is simply us.

Go into the negotiation room educated and collaborative for the best results. Know your worth and go get'em!

ADVANCING YOUR CAREER

Be strategic with your career moves. You can advance your job title and salary by asking periodically for a raise and/or promotion. Weigh the benefits of being promoted with the new tasks you may be asked to do. A lot of people also speed up their advancement and/or salary by switching jobs, but you don't want to switch jobs too often because it then makes you look unstable and unattractive to new potential employers. Ideally stick with a job for two years before changing. That being said, employers understand the hardships that jobs might present with special circumstances, such as management overturning frequently or other strenuous situations.

INCREASING SKILLS

Wisdom is knowing what to do next, skill is knowing how to do it, and virtue is doing it.

- David Starr Jordan

ADDING SKILLS TO YOUR TOOL BELT

Learning new skills is important; for both your professional development and personal well-being. According to a Harvard Medical School article titled: "Learning A New Skill Can Slow Cognitive Aging," by Matthew Solan, practicing a new skill can stimulate new brain-cell growth.[5] An increase in the density of your myelin, or the white matter in your brain, helps improve performance, keeps you sharp, and can even fight off cognitive aging. Learning can come in many forms, but for now, let's look at learning new skills that can help you achieve your goals. The great thing about both soft and hard skills is that you can acquire them through education and practice.

SOFT SKILLS

Below are the top six soft skills that employers look for:
- Communication
- Teamwork
- Self-Management
- Problem Solving
- Resilience
- Positive Attitude

Are there any soft skills from this list that you'd like to improve?

....

....

How will you practice improving your soft skills?
Example: I will read *Nonviolent Communication* to increase my communication skills and find one suggestion from the book to practice over the next three months.

....

....

....

FULL POTENTIAL

HARD SKILLS

Hard skills are what is required to do a specific job. They are specified, clearly defined and quantified skills, which are usually work-related. Hard skills are most commonly evaluated during interviews, but it is your soft skills that can make you a desirable candidate over others and can drive home your likelihood of getting hired. Almost any skill can be attainable if you are willing to invest the time and effort to learn it. Acquiring new skills should be a lifelong practice and can lead to increased productivity, efficiency, advancement of your career and personal satisfaction.

Being an expert in a specific skill set can make you more valuable to your potential employer. The types of hard skills you need to possess depend on the job you are applying for. However, there are some general hard skills most employers look for, such as being able to use a spreadsheet or proficiency with typing.

What hard skills would you like to gain that can help you obtain your career goals? Not sure? Look online at job postings to see what skills employers are looking for or research professionals on LinkedIn to see what kinds of skills they list in their profile.

1.

2.

3.

How do you plan on learning more about your industry and staying on top of trends? (Get specific, such as the "How I Built This" Podcast to learn more about entrepreneurship)

PLACES TO INCREASE HARD SKILLS:

College: For some career goals a more formalized degree may be necessary. You can also check out local community colleges to gain specific skills without having to get a full degree. Another resource is bootcamp academies, such as General Assembly, that offer short immersive trainings and certifications.

Online Universities: Most universities offer online courses. You can gain credentials from major universities, such as Harvard or U.C. Berkeley, through taking online courses. There are also websites such as Coursera.org or EdX. org that offer courses from numerous universities.

Apps and websites: There are all kinds of apps and websites available to help you learn just about anything. For example, learn for free how to speak a new language through DuoLingo or learn how to code for free via CodeAcademy. LinkedIn Learning is also a great resource for multiple industries.

YouTube: What can't you find on YouTube nowadays? Learning new skills is certainly feasible through watching tutorials.

Certification programs: There are lots of certification programs that offer training in specialized areas of interest. Try typing in Google: certification for _____(skill or industry of interest).

Learn from others: Learn skills from friends, colleagues, mentors, industry professionals, etc. Learning from people who have experience can give you better insight into real world application of skills and can provide you information beyond what teaching programs may have to offer.

FULL POTENTIAL

NETWORKING

You can make more friends in two months by becoming interested in other people than you can in two years by trying to get other people interested in you.

- Dale Carnegie

After teaching networking to people of all ages and backgrounds, I've discovered that most people are reluctant to network. The word "networking" tends to have a negative, or uncomfortable feeling associated with it. People tend to think of networking as a selfish act of wanting to gain something from someone. I see networking as a connected interaction of supporting one another rather than a one-sided gain.

The Cambridge Dictionary defines networking as "the process of meeting and talking to a lot of people, especially in order to get information that can help you.[6]"

I define networking as, "Genuinely getting to know someone and building a meaningful connection where you can help each other."

Do you see the difference? Cambridge's definition is what we all dislike about the idea of networking - manipulation and using others for our own gain. People can sense when you are talking to them only because you want something, making the exchange distasteful and empty. No one likes being used and you are unlikely to get good results with this approach. It is okay to approach people with an intended objective; in fact the best way to engage is to know why you are engaging and the results you want to achieve. However, it is most fruitful to approach others first and foremost to get to know them and develop a relationship. For example, while on a date, your objective might be to find a long-term relationship. On the first date, you know your intentions, but you do not immediately jump into a relationship. You first get to know that person, and then over time you build towards the results you want to achieve.

Listening, paired with curiosity, is key in networking. I have yet to meet a person who does not have an interesting story. Learning about people's journeys can offer new perspectives and knowledge. This is true whether you engage in a conversation with the corner-store cashier or the CEO of a multi-billion-dollar tech company. I have left conversations amazed and inspired after hearing about people's backgrounds and life's journeys. I have also had my preconceived notions of people shattered in unexpected ways after taking the time to get to know them.

FULL POTENTIAL

See if you can find topics that the other person enjoys speaking about. There are suggested questions for networking further along in this section. Pay attention to what topics light a person up and/or where they want to share a lot. Once you find those topics, dig deeper and activate your own curiosity on the topic. What would you like to know more about regarding the subject? You can also explore new perspectives by stepping into another person's world and interests. You never know what you might learn. If you become genuinely interested in someone's life, it can lead to conversations you've never imagined having and foster deeply rooted connections.

Maya Angelou said, "I've learned that people will forget what you said, people will forget what you did, but people will never forget how you made them feel." When it comes down to it, we are all motivated by things that make us feel good. Why would you want to connect with or help someone out who didn't leave a positive impression? As mentioned in the Getting Hired section of this guidebook, on average 80% of jobs are not advertised. Instead these jobs are filled through internal networks. Typically the most sought-after jobs are never even listed publicly, or if they are, it is merely a legal courtesy that they are obligated to perform. Building your network can be an essential step towards landing a job.

Take a moment to remember a conversation you've had on a topic that you had zero interest in. Did you want to continue the conversation? Did you feel connected to the person you were speaking with? How did you feel physically? How did you feel emotionally? Did you want to meet with this person again?

Now take a moment to recall a conversation on a topic you enjoy speaking about. Same questions. Did you want to continue the conversation? Did you feel connected to the person you were speaking with? How did you feel physically? How did you feel emotionally? Did you want to meet with this person again?

Which scenario would be more memorable? Who would you have a stronger connection to? Who would you give your contact information to in order to set up a meeting in the future?

Shifting your mindset to being inquisitive and authentic with your interactions will most likely make you more effective and less ambivalent with networking. Networking provides an essential opportunity to build your connections, which is a significant factor in achieving career and life goals. The longer I live the more I find that people are the key to just about everything in life. This is true both personally and professionally. As a single mom, I had to network to create a community of support. As an entrepreneur, my network has helped me obtain significant resources and funding. As a fun loving person, my network has provided free tickets to major shows and other fun perks. I have found the age-old saying to be true: it's not what you know, it's who you know.

What is your biggest fear or resistance with networking?

What are some ways to reframe your fear or resistance? Are there different ways to approach networking that can help mitigate your fear or resistance?

FULL POTENTIAL

CURRENT NETWORK

You network all the time; you just might not call it networking. If you are connecting to people on social media, you are networking. If you are talking to the people in the seats next to you at a sports game or entertainment show, you are networking. There are many ways you are already networking. You may be shocked to find that the connections you are looking for are much closer than expected. Many times I have had a student from my nonprofit tell the class something they are in need of (e.g. a summer job, tickets to a concert, information about a college). Within a class of thirty students living in a high-poverty neighborhood, we could find connections to meet all of their requests. These are kids who may be living out of their cars and for some, even though they live 20 miles away from San Francisco, have never visited the city. So imagine what your network may be able to provide.

In order to tap into your own dynamic network, start planting seeds by letting your network know what you are looking for. This is different than networking with people you don't know. It is okay to ask the people already in your life if they can help you. They of course have the choice to help you or not. It is important to respect their decision and not take it personally if they can't help you out, but from my experience the majority of people tend to enjoy being helpful. You never know who may be able to assist you. Your friend's next-door neighbor may be a manager for the company you would like to work for and can help you land a job. Support can come from unexpected places.

Mapping out your network is a great tool for figuring out how to connect to people who can be a helpful resource.

1ST-DEGREE CONNECTIONS:

List the people that support you the most. How can they help you find a job or obtain a specific goal? Example: My aunt works at Company X and can submit my resumé for the marketing role.

2ND-DEGREE CONNECTIONS:

Who in your network may have connections to help you obtain your goal? Example: My friend knows someone at Company X and he will introduce me to his connection.

3RD-DEGREE CONNECTIONS:

Who are some people you would like to add into your network, or specific key people that can help you obtain your goal? Example: The Director of Marketing at Company X.

FULL POTENTIAL

EXPANDING YOUR NETWORK

The best way to expand your network is to get clear on your intention of why you're wanting to connect with people. It could be that you want to develop a group of friends who enjoy outdoor activities, or you are wanting to learn more about how nonprofits function or land that dream job. There are many reasons for wanting to connect with people. The clearer you are on reasons why you want to meet new people, the more likely you will gain higher-quality connections.

Here are some suggestions on how to expand your network:

- Ask someone you already know for an introduction, or post on social media to see if your friends can help you out with a connection.
- Go to an event or convention related to your interests and meet new people.
- Create networking goals for yourself - example: have coffee with a new person each week. You can even create a ripple effect with expanding your network by letting the people you meet with know about your goal and asking them if they know of someone they think would be a good fit to introduce you to. Be upfront with expressing why you want to meet new people and what you hope to learn or gain from the meetings. This will help with connecting you to the right people.
- Chat with the person sitting next to you at a coffee shop, restaurant, sports events, etc.
- Join online groups related to what your interests are.
- Take a class or get involved with an activity or hobby that is interactive.

STARTING NETWORKING CONVERSATIONS

Level 1: Start conversations with a basic introduction.

Level 2: Next, you can ask questions relevant to where you are. "What is it that you enjoy by participating with this group?" or "What do you hope to gain through your time at this event?" or "Is this your preferred coffee shop?"

Engage in listening and ask a couple of follow up questions. Here are some examples of the beginning of good follow-up questions:

- Can you tell me more about...
- What would you do if...
- What did you mean by...
- How else might you...
- When was the last time you...
- How are you going to...
- Why do you think...

Level 3: You can then transition into deeper questions, which will leave a lasting impression and create much stronger bonds. The more vulnerable you are in the conversation, the more people will open up to you.

Questions for in-depth conversations:

- What is one interesting thing you learned this week?
- What is something that you are passionate about?
- How do you want to leave this world a better place?
- What's something you're looking forward to?
- Who has had the biggest influence on your life?
- What would constitute a "perfect" day for you?
- If you could meet anyone, dead or alive, who would that be and why?
- What's something you want to accomplish before this year is over?
- If you could go to one place in the world, where would you want to travel to?
- If you didn't do what you're doing now, what kind of job would you have?
- What is a song that you relate to the most and why?
- What are some things on your bucket list?
- What do you feel the most grateful for in your life?
- What is the greatest accomplishment in your life?

Try picking one or two of these questions or come up with your own. Write your questions in the notes section of your phone for reference when you are out and wanting to engage in a conversation. Remember to engage your curiosity and ask follow-up questions.

FULL POTENTIAL

MANAGING YOUR PROFESSIONAL NETWORK

I recommend building meaningful work related relationships with one to three people who could provide good guidance, and who believe in you and support your life goals. For everyone else, add them as a contact on LinkedIn, where you can access them when you need specific support. You have only so much time that you can allocate to building connections. You do not want to spread yourself too thin creating lots of okay relationships. Quality relationships are far more beneficial than unrealistically trying to develop in-depth relationships with many.

CHALLENGE - GO TO A NETWORKING EVENT!

Write your experience below. What worked, and what didn't work? What would you want to change or keep the same for the next networking event?

MENTORSHIP & SPONSORSHIP

The best people to be part of your support system are people who accept your past, support your present and encourage your future.

- Unknown

FINDING A MENTOR

Having an experienced and trusted advisor to guide you in the right direction is incredibly valuable for advancing your career. According to a survey by the American Society for Training and Development, 75% of executives say mentoring has been critical to their career development.[7] A good mentor provides information and guidance, helps you see areas where you could improve, gives encouragement, is someone you can contact when you need advice, is a good sounding board, and advances your personal and professional growth.

I met my mentor when he was a guest lecturer in one of my classes at U.C. Berkeley. At that point in my life I had no idea what a mentorship relationship looked like. Fortunately my mentor had mentored others in the past and had an excellent structure for our relationship. My mentor was not in the same field as I was. He was a successful entrepreneur in the automotive business and I was in the middle of founding a nonprofit. However, I admired his approach to business. His advice was universal. He had ingenious logic balanced with high emotional intelligence and he had lots of great tips and tools that helped me improve my business skills. Most importantly he was invested in my success. I truly couldn't have asked for a better mentor. A good mentor or sponsor has the ability to see what others, or even yourself, may have not seen...yet and is able to help you navigate how to reach your full potential. Here are some things I learned from him and from my research on mentorship relationships:

Factors to consider when looking for a mentor:
- You feel like their personality fits with yours.
- Lives in close proximity so that they can potentially introduce you to local resources.
- You admire their approach to their career and life.
- Has the title, position or experience you're hoping to achieve in the next few years.

Your mentor should:
- Respect you and be invested in your success.
- Be a good listener and provide constructive feedback.

- Does not force their disposition on you, but instead views their advice as an offering, which you can choose to accept or decline without them taking offense.
- Understands that your personal and professional life influence each other.
- Challenge you to achieve greater success.

Identifying your ideal mentor:
- Write down people you think of as potential mentors.
- If you don't personally know someone, you can research people who are accessible (not the CEO of Google).
- Go to conferences, talks or events where high caliber people attend.
- Ask people you already know if they know of someone who would serve as a good mentor.

Suggestions for asking someone to be your mentor:

Be specific with what you are looking for in a mentor. That way they know what they are signing up for and you get what it is you need. Having a strong sense of your needs can help both of you to make sure it will work well. Emphasize why you think he/she would make a good mentor and what you hope to gain through working together. Don't be afraid to ask questions to make sure it is the right fit. The best mentorship relationship has a clear agreement. Most people who would make a good mentor are busy people, so you want to make sure to respect their time and adapt your schedule to theirs as opposed to having them adjust their schedule to yours. Ideally, you will want to ask in person whether she/he would be willing to mentor you. Here are some questions you can ask yourself before approaching a potential mentor:

What are your mentorship needs?

FULL POTENTIAL

How often and for how long will you be meeting/talking?

Example: once a month for a thirty-minute phone call and once every three months for a sixty-minute in-person meeting.

_____

_____

_____

_____

Do you want to have access to your mentor between meetings, and what is the preferred method of contact?

This may be a conversation to have with them.

_____

_____

_____

_____

What specifically do you hope to gain through your relationship?

_____

_____

_____

_____

Pay it forward and consider mentoring someone who is a couple of steps behind you. It is a highly rewarding experience!

FINDING A SPONSOR

A mentor advises and a sponsor advocates. It is important to understand the difference and the structure of these relationships. Mentors support your well-being and progression through listening, sharing knowledge, offering encouragement, and can provide the tools and contacts that help your personal and professional growth. Mentors are the people you can talk to about anything, including issues you shouldn't bring up with a colleague or sponsor, such as questioning your career or personal fears or doubts. A sponsor promotes you through using their connections and professional power to advocate for you. Many sponsors like to help because they believe in your potential and/or may see you as a protege. Their role is to proactively look for opportunities for you. Sponsors are actually more influential in your career advancement, but mentors play a quieter, yet still essential role in both your career and personal advancement.

Usually sponsors come from work environments, but that is not always the case. For the sponsor, it takes time to build trust and rapport with you in order to be a good advocate. You have to continuously deliver proof of your capabilities before a sponsor is willing to bring you under their wing. When searching for a sponsor, make sure to look for people who have the ability to advance your career, not just people you admire. In order to find a sponsor who won't waste your time and will deliver results, observe potential sponsors' accountability and track record with how they conduct business, and their interactions with others. It is worth considering finding more than one sponsor so you can have people champion you in different ways. Here are some questions to consider when looking for a sponsor:

- What are my long-term goals that a sponsor can help me with?
- Who would have the ability to advance my career?
- Who would benefit from my advancement?
- Who has a strong network and is connected to people that can advance my career?
- Do I know someone in a position of power who likes and trusts me?
- Who makes pay and promotion decisions?
- Who will make time to advocate for me?

MINDSET

If you change the way you look at things, the things you look at change.

- Wayne Dyer

THE IMPACT OF THOUGHTS

Your thoughts affect all aspects of your life, whether you are aware of them or not. Every experience begins with a thought. That thought, placed into action, creates a ripple effect that becomes magnified in your life. For example, I was feeling stuck with my nonprofit. Every day I was waking up not knowing where to focus my energy, and feeling incompetent. This made me want to not do anything at all. I decided it was time to change my mindset from being avoidant to being proactive. I realized that I was trying to fill a skill set that I was not aligned with. I began telling people what I was struggling with and that I was looking for someone to help me with program outreach. Immediately I felt a huge weight lifted off my shoulders. Then miraculous things started happening. In the most unexpected places, like in a shared car ride, I was finding solutions. I ended up meeting a highly experienced woman who was willing to volunteer her time while we found the funding to be able to transition her into a full-time position. When you start thinking and saying what you want then your mind automatically shifts and pulls you in that direction. That is why the practice of rewiring your thinking is key to your success and happiness.

Your brain has developed neural pathways associated with responses to situations. For example, if you have a time-sensitive task that needs completion, your immediate response might be to become stressed out. The stress response is formed by repeatedly feeling this way. We train ourselves to respond in the same fashion, regardless of whether or not the stress is warranted. The good news is that you have power and a choice regarding how you want to respond to any given situation. The process of choosing starts when you realize how you are feeling. Then you can redirect that feeling in order to create new neural pathways. A redirected response to feeling stressed out might be, "All I can do is my best with the time and resources I have. Compared to other situations in life this is not a big deal and doesn't justify my being stressed out."

Repetition is essential when creating new neural pathways. Your typical tendencies are engraved pathways in your brain, similar to a ski trail that has

FULL POTENTIAL

been used over and over. It is easy and natural to follow the established path. Going off the path is difficult, and in the beginning it is especially challenging to carve a new path. After you travel down a new route for some time, a new path begins to form. Eventually you can go down that new path with ease. That is exactly what happens in your brain when you practice a new thought pattern or behavior. New grooves are created and soon the formerly unfamiliar way of being becomes the norm.

Your mindset is one of the most influential forces moving you either away or towards achieving your goals. I have seen with my friends, family, and students that time and time again the biggest obstacle they face is themselves. How can you accomplish something you don't believe you are capable of accomplishing? Would you feel more inclined to help someone who might want to do something or someone who is ready and excited to do it? Believing in yourself creates much greater opportunity for people to believe in you and greater opportunity for you to step into your innate abilities and power.

Why is it then that we are always our own worst critics? We say and think things about ourselves that we would never think about others, even people we don't like. Our negative self-talk can be detrimental to our progress and poisonous to our health. Yet, we've all experienced negative self-talk. Neuroscientists have discovered that shame and self-criticism can reduce our prefrontal cortex's ability to sustain attention, increases impulsive behavior and leads to mental health issues such as depression and anxiety.[8]

We all have flaws and experience difficult situations in life; it's inevitable. No one escapes hardship and no one is perfect. It is good to know both your flaws and assets. You may even find that your flaws are sometimes assets and your assets are sometimes flaws. Kintsugi is the Japanese art of repairing pottery with a lacquer made from precious metals, to emphasize that an object can be more beautiful for having been broken. The philosophy of the art embraces the flaws, rather than trying to hide the damage. Everyone has imperfections. How we piece ourselves back together and find ways of improving is what truly matters. Close your eyes for thirty seconds and imagine how you would feel if you fully embraced and appreciated all aspects of yourself.

There is something to say for nurturing positive thoughts and the magnetism of good fortune that comes along with them. If you come from a place of fear and negative thinking, your interactions will reflect that. If your mindset is positive, that will be reflected back to you as well. By placing your attention on the positive, you will naturally start to gravitate towards attracting good things into your life. Be your own best advocate and remember that whatever you say to yourself you are reinforcing.

> *Whether you think you can,*
> *or think you can't - you're right.*
> *- Henry Ford*

Doing anything new is usually both scary and exciting. The fascinating thing about fear is that on the flip side of fear is usually excitement. Fear can indicate that something matters to you. However, fear that is unexamined can stunt your growth and ability to reach your goals. It's important not to bury your fears. They will always find a way of popping back up in unexpected and sneaky ways. Instead, try to understand them. Even the feelings that most people would consider "bad" have value. For example, "I'm not good enough" can be a protective thought, helping make sure you are prepared to take on a task. Understanding your thoughts and their validity is key to giving you greater control of your reactions.

What fears, negative self-talk, mindsets, or barriers stand in the way of achieving your ideal life? Are there things you say to yourself, or things others say to you, that might get in the way of your success?

_____

_____

_____

_____

_____

Let's address them!

FULL POTENTIAL

Use a separate piece of paper to explore your thoughts. Explore only one thought at a time. Using two different colored pens (one assigned to questions and one assigned to answers), examine your fear(s) or doubt(s):

1. Using one color ask questions, such as:

- Why do I feel this way?
- Is this feeling connected to this situation or is it coming from somewhere else?
- Why is this thought wanting to hold me back?
- What is my worst-case scenario and what are the chances of it happening?
- Am I willing to ask for (and in some cases pay for) the support I need?

2. With the other color, answer your questions.

3. Keep going! If you feel stuck, try repeating "why?" and "what?" questions. Ask and answer questions until you feel like you have gone as far as you can go.

After journaling, what are your main discoveries?

SUGGESTIONS FOR SHIFTING YOUR THINKING

- Write down a positive statement to replace the negative thought. Writing down a new way of thinking, in advance, helps embed the thought in your mind for when reactions occur.
- You may want to place a visual reminder, such as a word or symbol, in the area you are most likely to have these negative thoughts.

Listen

Ignoring negative self-talk may seem like a good way to go about getting rid of it. However, negative thoughts don't just disappear. You may not be able to get rid of them, but you can control the volume. In order to have more control of these thoughts, you need to explore them. Negative thoughts aren't always bad. They can act as an alarm to alert us when something needs our attention. Then we can prepare to rectify the situation. It's helpful to observe your thoughts and emotions with non-judgemental openness and receptivity. Once you understand your thoughts you can determine whether or not they have validity. When you understand your thoughts and feelings you can make wiser choices and have more control of your actions.

Track

Keep a journal to document the times you are experiencing negative self-talk. Notice when you are saying things to yourself that you would never dream of saying to someone you care about. See if what you are saying to yourself has any validity or is helpful. If your thoughts are not valid or helpful, then you can decide to address them in a different way. When you're feeling bad about yourself or judging your shortcomings, pause to interrupt and disrupt your thoughts by bringing in new thoughts. You can create new neural pathways by practicing different ways of responding.

Kindness

We are told to be kind to ourselves, but it's taboo in some cultures, to say anything self-complementary. When we do then some people may think we are being arrogant. There is nothing arrogant about admitting our strengths. It's important to be as comfortable examining our strengths as well as our weaknesses.

Being kind to yourself, especially during hard times, does not mean being self pitying or self indulgent. Self-compassion is empowering, whereas self-pity is falling into a victim role. The goal of this guidebook is for you to become fully empowered, accountable and engaged in all aspects of your life. When you are having a hard day, or going through a difficult time, be kind to yourself. You can ask yourself, "How can I care for myself?" or, "How would I care for a friend going through this situation?"

What are some things you can do to practice self-care?
Example: Getting out in nature, buying fresh flowers, going for a motorcycle ride, etc.

....

....

....

HARDSHIPS

Chasing after your dreams can present hardships. I believe that when faced with hardships, people have three choices: advance, stay neutral, or digress. Advancing is the most difficult choice, but also the most rewarding. Obstacles and hardships are normal. It is really tough to be in a situation where you have little or no control, especially if what is happening has a large impact on your life. The best thing to do is embrace the things you have no control over. There are many angles from which to approach situations, and sometimes it takes out-of-the-box thinking. Redirecting your attention from that which is immovable allows you to shift your focus to a world filled with new possibilities. When you surrender your resistance, the situation begins to shift. Here are some perspectives that help me when I'm going through difficult times:

1. Knowing it will pass and that you will not feel this way forever.

2. Approaching the hardship with curiosity. For example, when the economy tanked in 2009, my savings was depleted and no one was hiring within my industry. I was a single mother with no way of supporting my family. My stress began to transform into depression. I decided to be curious about what depression felt like in my body, my emotions, and the thoughts that were repeating in my mind. Not only did I examine the pain, I also examined what took me out of the pain. What I found helpful was being out in nature or connecting to sensations, like the feeling of my bare feet on the ground, or taking a big breath whenever I felt in a state of overwhelm. Instead of being passive I became engaged with my feelings, which opened up the opportunity to transform my situation.

3. Knowing when to step into and when to step out of your feelings is important. Taking a balanced approach, where your feelings are neither suppressed nor exaggerated, creates endurance. Be aware if you feel like you are going too far into your feelings and need to be pulled back out. If you are having a hard time doing this on your own, ask for help.

4. During hard times you can experiment with employing an inquisitive, adventurous and playful mindset. By doing this, the situation becomes more interesting and you are more likely to be engaged. You may want to test different approaches, such as examining the situation from different angles, exploring what you can learn, improving how you handle future situations, and playing with how you approach people and their responses. For example, if it is taking longer than expected to land a job and you're getting frustrated, you can try being playful with how you approach interviews. In your interviews, rather than having the conversation be all about you landing a job, you can turn the interview into an opportunity to get to know another person and how the company they work for approaches business. Most importantly, play redirects your attention from the outcome to making the process more enjoyable. This allows you to be more easygoing, which usually delivers much more satisfying results.

FULL POTENTIAL

PERSEVERANCE

Do not judge me by my successes; judge me by how many times I fell down and got back up again.

- Nelson Mandela

GRIT

Dr. Angela Duckworth is well known for her research on grit. Grit is the tendency to sustain interest and effort towards long-term goals. She found that grit is a better measure of a person's potential success than IQ or inherent talent.[9] There are many naturally talented people who don't end up reaching their full potential, while less-talented people accomplish remarkable things. Being persistent and intentional will yield results, but it takes courage and effort.

Characteristics of grit include:

- Courage and not being afraid of failure.
- Resilience and adaptability; staying with a task and not giving up.
- Striving for excellence, but not perfection.
- Showing commitment, pride, and a positive attitude while completing tasks.
- Patience and the willingness to work hard towards long-term goals.

At the root of grit is perseverance. Perseverance is embedded in nature. It's what helps all living things survive and thrive. Penguins endure -70 degree weather. They do this by huddling together and rotating members of the group into the middle to get warm, all the while warming their eggs beneath them. Trees shape themselves around objects that are in the way of their roots so they can continue to grow. Perseverance is all around us and also inherent within each one of us. Just as there are different forms of perseverance in nature, humans also take different approaches to overcoming obstacles.

We are now going to explore ways to increase your perseverance and how you approach challenges!

FINDING WAYS TO INCREASE PERSERVERANCE

Think back to a time when you were unable to overcome a challenge that you wanted to accomplish. What would you do differently?

Some things you can ask yourself:

- What were you feeling at the time?
- What resources would have been helpful? (ex. research, people, materials, legal aide, non-profit support)
- What were some questions that would have been helpful to ask people?
- What resources did you need to overcome this challenge?
- At what point did you give up?
- What would it have looked like if it were possible to overcome the challenge?
- What was within your power to change and what was not within your power to change?

HOW YOU OVERCAME A CHALLENGE

Can you remember a specific time in your life when you overcame a challenge?

- What motivated you to move through the situation?
- What were the actions you took that were helpful?
- What resources did you rely on?
- Who or what helped transform the situation?
- What changes did you make to overcome the challenge?
- What habits did you rely on to succeed?
- Looking back, what are some things you would do differently?
- What past experiences prepared you to overcome this challenge?

FULL POTENTIAL

YOUR APPROACH TO PERSEVERANCE

Summarize your personal approach to perseverance:

- What motivates you to keep going?
- What qualities/skills do you use to persevere when things get hard?
- What tactics do you use to overcome hardships?

INCREASING PERSEVERANCE

Embracing the struggle, learning from setbacks and moving forward (when moving forward is the healthy and most aligned choice) will build your resilience and boost your chances of success. Here are some tips on increasing your perseverance:

- Developing a fascination: Bringing wonder and curiosity into your work will allow you to be more engaged and less likely to give up.
- Daily improvements: The secret of your success is in your daily routines. Take action every day to reach your highest potential.
- Bigger purpose: Connect to the purpose, or larger meaning, that your work has in the world or in your life.
- Growth mindset: A belief that you have the capacity to develop skills, intellect and talent through practice and perseverance.

WHEN TO PERSEVERE AND WHEN TO LET GO

There can be huge benefits to pursuing your goals in the face of hardships and setbacks. There are also times when it's better to redirect your energy and efforts. Below are some tips for discerning when to let things go and when to keep persisting.

Questions to ask yourself:

- Why did you want to pursue this goal to begin with and has anything changed?
- Are your efforts in service to your long-term goals?
- Are your goals in alignment with who you are?
- Are you lacking resources or information to achieve your goals?
- Is your goal creating unnecessary stress and hardship? Is it in your best interest to change course?
- What would you tell someone else going through the same situation?

Tools:

You can use as few or as many of the following tools as you would like. The more tools you use, the more clarity you will gain.

- Pros and cons list.
- Take a break and revisit your choices once you have refreshed your thinking. A break could be something like a walk or a weekend getaway.
- Talk to people about what you're debating and get different perspectives.
- Get all the resources or information you may be missing before you decide to do something different.
- Ask yourself questions using the two-colored-pen method mentioned in the Mindset section.
- Personal **SWOT** analysis (using the example of becoming a singer); listing your personal **STRENGTHS** (Example: great voice), **WEAKNESSES** (Example: scared of crowds), the industry **OPPORTUNITIES** (Example: living in LA with lots of record labels) and **THREATS** (Example: saturated industry).
- Consider your alternatives and weigh all factors.
- Journal.
- Ask for help.

GRATITUDE

Gratefulness is the key to a happy life that we hold in our hands, because if we are not grateful, then no matter how much we have we will not be happy — because we will always want to have something else or something more.

~ Dr. David Steindl-Rast

PRACTICING GRATITUDE

Practicing gratitude is an easy and highly effective way to increase your happiness and find meaning in your everyday life. The Happier Human, a website dedicated to science-backed happiness analysis, reviewed thirty-seven sources and studies finding that:[10]

- A five-minute daily gratitude journal can increase your well-being by more than 10%, which is the same increase of well-being if you were to double your income.
- Gratitude creates a happier demeanor and in turn increases your social attractiveness. People who are 10% more grateful than the average person have 17.5% more social capital, which is beneficial personally and also helpful when networking to get jobs.
- Gratitude increases your physical health. This Includes better sleep, fewer physical ailments and increased mental health, giving you more energy to get ahead in life.
- Gratitude can help advance your career. Being grateful for the people and environment around you creates likeability and allies. Benefits can include: developing a positive reputation, helping you network and find mentors, broadening your decision-making capabilities, increasing productivity, furthering achievement of goals, and making the workplace more enjoyable for yourself and others.

Practicing gratefulness is an excellent tool for managing stress and overcoming challenges. Every day we are surrounded by positive encounters and events, even on what feels like our worst days. Taking a pause in your day to recognize the good things happening will help you rewire your brain to look for the good in life. Spend a few minutes each day to practice gratitude. I recommend doing this either first thing in the morning or right before you go to sleep. You can also share your gratitude for others by sending an email, texting or calling someone you appreciate, which will make their day. By practicing gratitude you will live a much more fulfilled and motivated life.

Fill in the answers below to practice gratitude. You can use this exercise or find a different format that works best for your daily gratitude practice.

What are you most grateful for?

I am grateful for _____ that happened today.

I am grateful for _____ within myself or that I did.

I am grateful for _____ in my relationships.

I am grateful for _____ in my professional life.

I am grateful for _____ in my health.

I am grateful for (name of friend)_____

Because_____

_____

_____

I am grateful for (name of family member)_____

Because_____

_____

_____

I am grateful for (current or past colleague)_____

Because_____

_____

_____

RECOGNITION

When was the last time you recognized your successes and acknowledged how far you have come? In my experience, when I'm not aware of the progression I have made towards accomplishing my goal, or in my life in general, I feel stagnant and lose motivation. Periodically reflecting on what I have achieved refreshes my drive for accomplishing goals. It is also important to reflect on accomplishments as a team. Recognizing teammates, or work milestones, garners motivation, collaboration, and loyalty.

Think back to one year ago. **What have you achieved in this last year?**

FULL POTENTIAL

LOOKING BACK
AT YOUR LIFE
AT 100 YEARS OLD

The thrill is to keep envisioning what can be and then have the guts to go for it and make it real.

- Oprah Winfrey

Engage your imagination, and picture yourself at one-hundred years old. If you were to look back at your most perfect life, what kind of life did you live?

Using a blank piece of paper, write down your answers and then write a final statement in this guidebook. The questions below are there to spark your thinking, but don't feel like you have to answer all of them.

Where did you live? The more detail the better.

- Did you live in an apartment or a house?
- Did you live in a big city or a small town?
- Did you move from place to place at different points in your life?
- What was the environment you lived in?
- How would you have described your home? For example, aesthetics, outdoor area, plants, architecture, etc.

Who did you live your life with?

- Did you get married?
- Did you have children?
- Did you adopt any pets?
- What kind of friendships did you have?
- What kind of relationship did you have with your family?

What was your career like?

- Was your profession an important part of your identity?
- Did you stay in the same career your whole life or did you switch fields?
- How did your peers and those closest to you view your career?
- What was the highlight of your success?

What was most important to you?

- What brought you the most joy?
- What hobbies or pastimes did you enjoy?
- Did you find meaning in spending time with other people?
- Did you have any experiences that changed your life forever?
- How were you able to find happiness and/or confidence in your life?
- Were you healthy and fit?
- Did you spend time outdoors or traveling?
- How did you view the world?
- What bucket list items did you get to check off your list?

What did you contribute to the world?

- What did you bring into your community?
- Did you create a company that solves problems?
- Did you engage in volunteering activities?
- Did you leave a person or place better than how you found it?
- What do you want to be remembered for?

YOUR LIFE STORY

YOUR LIFE STORY

FULL POTENTIAL

TIPS FOR
THE DIFFERENT
STAGES OF LIFE

*Every next level of your life
will demand a different you.*

- Leonardo DiCaprio

THE DIFFERENT STAGES OF LIFE

Throughout a lifetime of interacting with people in business, friendship, dating, being a parent, and observing kids demeanors, I can wholeheartedly say that age does not determine maturity or capability. I have witnessed seventeen-year-olds run businesses and seventy-year-olds not only learn, but also teach trending business skills. It is never too early or too late to decide to do something you love.

The disparity between how you feel and how you are perceived can be problematic at times. I know when I was a twenty-year-old entrepreneur I was not taken as seriously as I am now that I am in my late thirties. I look back at some of the business proposals I had then and they are well thought out and have a lot of potential. On the other side of the spectrum, I hear stories from my mom about how men she knows who write scripts for movies and television shows in Los Angeles have to dye their hair to be considered relevant. However, we can not let society's perception of age dictate our potential success. At times we may have to work harder to prove our value, but once value is seen, even in just one situation or by just one influential person, that value tends to stick and carry forward into other situations.

Of course, we each go through stages of development throughout our lifetime. This guidebook is relevant for all those stages. I have spent extensive time researching how to best guide you with whatever stage of life stage you are at. In the following sections, I do however, focus on bigger life events where specific guidance is helpful. Feel free to jump into whatever section feels most relevant to you. You may also find value in reading all the sections. There are tips in each section that can easily spill over into all age groups. No matter what stage of life you are at, the determining factor of your success is you.

PREPARING
FOR YOUR FIRST JOB
AFTER COLLEGE

*Do what you have to do, to
do what you want to do.*

- Denzel Washington

YOUR FIRST JOB

It's never too early to map out a promising job trajectory. Entering the workforce for the first time can be intimidating. If you are feeling uneasy when you think about your next steps after graduation, you're not alone. It may feel uncomfortable for a period of time as you are figuring everything out. This is normal and it will pass.

First jobs tend to be at an entry level. The pay may be meager and the tasks may not be exciting. This is just part of the process most people experience on the path towards attaining their ultimate goal. Keep a positive attitude and take this time as an opportunity to learn as much as you can. Stay at your first job for at least one year before transitioning to a different company. This not only shows your next employer that you are stable and reliable, but also allows you to get a fuller picture of the job. If you find yourself in need of workplace guidance, seek out the right people to ask for help (that can be a mentor, colleague, family member, friends, etc.). Don't be ashamed to ask for support. We all need help at times. It is better to ask for support than to make avoidable mistakes, waste time trying to figure things out by yourself, or end up shutting down and not doing anything at all.

Use Your School's Career Services

Schools are there to help you succeed at finding a job. When you're successful, they're successful. Make an appointment with your advisor, check in with your career center and go to career fairs to find opportunities. Increase your personal network by taking advantage of your school's alumni database. Career counselors can potentially provide introductions to alumni in similar fields. You can also look up individuals or alumni groups on places such as LinkedIn. Your alumni network can be one of the most valuable resources you have for landing a job.

Resumé Tips

List any classes you have taken that relate to the specific job you are applying for. Add your GPA if it is above 3.5, but not if it is under. List extracurricular activities such as: clubs, volunteer work, case competitions, hackathons, etc.

FULL POTENTIAL

Internships

While in school, take advantage of internship opportunities. You can also participate in internships during the summer or right after you graduate. You may want to consider finding an internship with a company that has wide brand recognition. Having a brand name on your resume adds credibility and opens doors. Through internships you can gain skills, develop contacts and, most importantly, help with receiving a job offer.

LinkedIn

Employers are looking on LinkedIn. A study by Omnicore showed that only 25% of 18-25 year olds are on LinkedIn[1] Creating a LinkedIn profile helps you stand out from the competition. You can add the personal brand statement you created in this guidebook and describe what you aspire to do with your career. Include in your profile extra-curricular activities, accolades, and any jobs you may have had - even if they were in unrelated fields. Procuring recommendations from people who value your work adds credibility to your profile. This is a unique opportunity to provide this information to future employers, which can help you get your foot in the door.

Other Online Presence

To stand out, you can increase your online presence by:
- Writing blog posts
- Building an online portfolio
- Creating a personal website
- Joining online communities
- Contributing good-quality content to posts

You may also want to consider editing your social media posts or making your account private.

CAREER TRANSITIONS

Honor the space between no longer and not yet.

- Nancy Levin

TRANSITIONING CAREERS

Congratulations on having the courage to explore changes that will increase your happiness! In the long run this can be the best thing you can do for yourself. In the short term, major career transitions might disrupt your life and be challenging. You can choose to take small steps or you can take big bounds when transitioning careers. If you prefer stability, you may want to take small steps and maintain your current job as you gain the skills necessary to move into a new position. Another option is to find a company that has room for career advancement. You can apply for a role with your current title and over time transition into your preferred role. Glassdoor.com is a great resource for researching companies that offer career advancement. If you're ready to take a leap and go all in, you can potentially expedite transitioning your career. This is more of a lionhearted approach. Making a clean break can be powerful and exciting, but be prepared for potential bumps along your path.

You may be moving into a new career after taking a break from the workforce. Reentering the workforce can be difficult, but there are more and more initiatives available to assist with reentry. Many people make the mistake of jumping into the first job they find. Reentering the workforce is an opportunity for a reboot. I encourage you to take the time to pursue what you really want to be doing in the next chapter of your life. You'll likely have to explain why you had time away from the workforce. Keep the explanation of your hiatus brief and emphasize any skills you built during your break. For example, "It was important to be home with my child for the first year. During this time I volunteered as a marketing manager where I gained skills related to photoshop, social media best practices, etc." Volunteering is a good way to gain work experience that you can then put on your resumé.

The two most important things you can do when transitioning careers are:

1) Activate your network
2) Understand your transferable skills

Through interviewing Human Resource professionals and individuals who successfully transitioned careers I was able to distill some key tips.

Activate Your Network

Your network can vouch for your work ethic and skills, as well as connect you to people and opportunities.

- Start by asking the people who know you best for help because they will be your greatest advocates.
- It's easy to overlook contacts that could be helpful. Look through your phone or social media contacts to identify people who it might be advantageous to connect with.
- Make it effortless for people in your network to support you. If you have identified someone in <u>their</u> network that you would like to be introduced to, you can offer to create an email that you write in <u>their voice</u> for them to send to their contact. Keep the email short and concise. In your contacts perspective, highlight who you are, the reasons you want to be introduced to them and ask if their contact would be willing to speak with you.

Increase Your Network

I cannot emphasise this enough - it's not what you know, it's who you know. Getting the right introductions can accelerate the process of landing a job.

- Use informational interviews with people in your field of interest to learn how your current skills could transfer into jobs. You can ask, "My skill set is _____; what positions in your field use this skill set?" You don't want to conduct this sort of informational interview with someone at your ideal company because it could make you look like an unqualified candidate.
- Research the hiring manager. See if there is a way to be introduced to them in order to have a conversation about your candidacy as a future employee. Make sure to have a compelling statement about why you are a good candidate for the position.
- Going to industry conferences is a great way to meet people and learn the newest trends.
- Revisit the Networking section in this guidebook.

Match Transferable Skills

A transferable skill is an aptitude or knowledge that you have used in previous work, which can translate into skills needed for a different position. For

example, if you were a waiter or waitress you probably developed strong people skills, which is useful in any position where there is human interaction. The key is to be able to convey what you did in a clever way that relates to the job you're interested in. For example, "Provided exemplary service in a high-volume upscale restaurant, where I gained many interpersonal skills, including xyz."

- Match job descriptions with your transferable skills. On a piece of paper list all the skills that are needed for the job you're interested in. Leave space next to the job's "required skills" to write in how your past experience is applicable to these skills.
- Identify and emphasize transferable skills on your resume and LinkedIn profile.
- Outside perspectives can help you see your skills in a new way. Ask friends how they think your previous experience transfers to the skills needed for the position you are hoping to gain.

Gain New Skills

- Enhance your education. There are many ways to do this: workshops, trainings, bootcamps, certification programs, college, etc.
- You may want to think about whether or not the time and money you need to spend on education is worth your investment or if there is an alternative path that will lead to your desired result.
- Volunteering for a nonprofit is an easy and low-risk way to experience a new career and gain new skills. Look on sites such as volunteermatch.org or reach out directly to nonprofits you are interested in.

Tell A Compelling Story

It is up to you to paint a picture of who you are to make yourself a compelling candidate. Craft your narrative by thoughtfully picking the stories that you want to share at opportune times.

- Be prepared with the five essential things you want someone to know about you which are relatable to landing the job. You can sprinkle these five things into your conversation.
- Be prepared before having important conversations. Practice what you will say before approaching your targeted companies.

VEKITA

- Be clear about what you want to do and why.
- Align your story with the job description.
- Let the hiring manager know that you're serious and committed to mastering the craft related to the job, and why it's important to you.
- You can experiment and refine how you tell your story with each consecutive conversation. You can also alter your presentation as you notice how people with different personality types differ in their response to your story.
- You and the hiring manager may be avoiding directly addressing the fact that you are transferring careers. You can be direct. Put on the table why they should consider you for the position and what makes you a better choice than other candidates. Only have this conversation in person - never over the phone.

Other Tips

- Understand the job market and research companies that can and are willing to invest in your transition.
- If your current skill set fits within a job that is close, but not exactly what you want to be doing, you can go for that job and work towards your ideal position.
- It's difficult to get hired by well-recognized companies because everyone wants those companies' names on their resume. You may want to consider working for a smaller or start-up business to gain the skills and experience needed before approaching larger named companies.
- Pursuing niches, or trending areas, within the industry you're interested in can be a great way to make yourself stand out and get your foot in the door.

Have patience with yourself through this process. Watch for frustration and be careful not to bring that into your conversations. There may be times when it feels like you are doing everything you can and nothing is happening. Stay the course! With perseverance something will eventually open up. You are building a life in which you can really be yourself and flourish. Remember to stay connected with your passion, purpose and why this is important to you.

FULL POTENTIAL

THE GOLDEN YEARS

You are never too old to set another goal or to dream a new dream.

- C.S. Lewis

Novelist George Eliot wrote, "It's never too late to be what you might have become." Regardless of what age you are, there are workforce entry challenges. If you are in your golden years you may have to face challenges, such as agism, physical changes, and/or a shift in motivation. Although these challenges are very real, they needn't stop you from doing what you love to do. An older worker also brings many strengths to the table.

Numerous studies have shown the value of employing older workers. The University of Michigan found that subjects in their sixties fared far better than younger adults at imagining different points of view, thinking of multiple resolutions, and suggesting compromises.[2] According to an article in Psychology Today, older minds make significantly better choices by using their prefrontal cortex, where more rational, deliberative thinking is controlled.[3] Other possible assets gained as we age are wisdom and knowledge from lessons learned. These are all solid reasons why you may be a great candidate for a job. As a person ages they may have more flexibility with their work options. The three primary paths are:

Retirement

If you are able to retire, this is an excellent opportunity to pursue dreams and passions that you might have put on hold. This may mean no longer waiting to write your book or go traveling. It may also mean contributing to meaningful causes, mentoring, or finding ways to share the wisdom you have gained through the years.

Part-Time Work

Many people over sixty have a pension plan or social security, but still need to supplement their income. It may be worth considering taking a part-time job or figuring out creative ways to make extra money, such as selling art, tutoring, pet-sitting, etc.

Full-Time Work

You may love working and want to remain in the workforce. As an older adult you may face ageism. The two strongest options for dealing with ageism are: 1) debunk misconceptions or, 2) go into fields that already value the wisdom that comes with age.

It's empowering to know about success stories of individuals in their golden years that are in your field. There are many great examples of successful older people in most fields. Researching individuals can be beneficial for your personal motivation, and the information may end up being helpful to tactfully share during an interview.

Potential employers may assume you are not up to speed on current industry knowledge. This makes it even more important for you to stay on the cutting edge of your field by being aware of industry trends. Be meticulous with how you present yourself by using strong talking points and quantitative data regarding why you would make a good candidate for the job. For example, if you are wanting to obtain a position as a software engineer, you can talk about success stories with previous work and your high scoring on code assessments. Finally, whether we say it or not, image matters. People will make assumptions about you based on your looks. For example, if you want to present yourself as a modern software engineer you have to also look the role. You may want to consider purchasing a trendy outfit for interviews.

Another smart tactic is to look for roles in industries where your age is respected and seen as valuable. Think about occupations that call for wisdom, such as a teacher or financial specialist. You can type "in-demand jobs for seniors" into a search engine to find good suggestions.

Tips For Competing In The Workforce

- To avoid age bias you do not have to reveal your age on your resumé. Resumés should only show the past 10 years of work experience, not your whole career and you do not have to include the year you graduated college.
- Stay relevant and current - consider taking an online certification or course to show that you are up to speed on the latest information and skills for your industry.
- AOL and Yahoo email addresses are considered outdated. Get yourself a Gmail or Outlook email address for sending emails to future employers.
- Make sure you have a digital presence with relevant content. Employers tend to do online searches on potential candidates. Create online profiles on sites such as LinkedIn, Medium, and/or Twitter.
- Having years of experience adds incredible value: Have your story about what you bring to the table prepared and why you should be hired versus someone younger.

Answering the following questions will help you articulate the unique value you bring into the workforce:

How has your sense of purpose and direction evolved as you've gained more life experience?

What holds meaning in your life today? How has that shifted over time?

FULL POTENTIAL

What are some of the most significant things you have learned throughout the years that can be applied to work?

_____

_____

_____

_____

_____

_____

What are you better at now than you were when you were younger?

_____

_____

_____

_____

_____

_____

_____

> *The great thing about getting older is that you don't lose all the other ages you've been behind.*
>
> *- Madeleine L'Engle*

Thank you for taking the time to go through this guidebook and for bringing your gifts into the world. I wish you boundless happiness and success as you begin a new chapter in your life.

For more information or for further support visit:

www.vekitapd.com

FULL POTENTIAL

NOTES

WHO YOU ARE

1   O'Keefe, P. A., Dweck, C. S., & Walton, G. M. (2018). Implicit Theories of Interest: Finding Your Passion or Developing It? Psychological Science, 29(10), 1653–1664. doi: 10.1177/0956797618780643

2   Flade, P., Asplund, J., & Elliot, G. (2020, February 28). Employees Who Use Their Strengths Outperform Those Who Don't. Retrieved form https://www.gallup.com/workplace/236561/employees-strengths-outperform-don.aspx

3   Kohanov, Linda (2017). Five Roles Of A Master Herder: a revolutionary model for socially intelligent leadership. Novato, CA: NEW WORLD LIBRARY.

WHAT YOU WANT IN YOUR LIFE

1   Workplace Stress Continues to Mount. (2018, November 14). Retrieved May 18, 2019, from https://www.kornferry.com/insights/articles/workplace-stress-motivation

2   Sorenson, S. (2020, January 30). How Employees' Strengths Make Your Company Stronger. Retrieved May 18, 2019, from https://www.gallup.com/workplace/231605/employees-strengths-company-stronger.aspx

3   Jebb, A. T., Tay, L., Diener, E., & Oishi, S. (2018). Happiness, income satisfaction and turning points around the world. Nature Human Behaviour, 2(1), 33–38. doi: 10.1038/s41562-017-0277-0

4   Duhigg, C. (2014). The Power Of Habit: why we do what we do in life and business. St. Louis, MO: Turtleback Books.

5   Hopper, E. (n.d.). Can Helping Others Help You Find Meaning in Life? Retrieved June 1, 2019, from https://greatergood.berkeley.edu/article/item/can_helping_others_help_you_find_meaning_in_life

ALIGNING WHO YOU ARE WITH YOUR CAREER

1   Todd, B. (2017, April 1). Job Satisfaction. Retrieved January 1, 2019, from https://80000hours.org/career-guide/job-satisfaction/

TOOLS FOR SUCCESS

1   CareerBuilder Survey. (2018, September 8). Retrieved from http://press. careerbuilder.com/2018-08-09-More-Than-Half-of-Employers-Have-Found-Content-on-Social-Media-That-Caused-Them-NOT-to-Hire-a-Candidate-According-to-Recent-CareerBuilder-Survey

2   Belli, G. (2019, March 4). How Many Jobs Are Found Through Networking, Really? Retrieved March 7, 2020, from https://www.payscale.com/career-news/2017/04/many-jobs-found-networking

3   Tarpey, M. (2018, January 9). How to master salary negotiation. Retrieved from https://www.careerbuilder.com/advice/how-to-master-salary-negotiation

4   Salary History Stats and Infographics. (n.d.). Retrieved April 1, 2019, from https://www.payscale.com/data/salary-history

5   Solan, M. (2016, April 27). Back to school: Learning a new skill can slow cognitive aging. Retrieved from https://www.health.harvard.edu/blog/learning-new-skill-can-slow-cognitive-aging-201604279502

6   NETWORKING: definition in the Cambridge English Dictionary. (n.d.). Retrieved March 8, 2020, from https://dictionary.cambridge.org/us/dictionary/english/networking

7   Council, Y. E. (2018, October 2). The Importance Of Mentorship. Retrieved from https://www.forbes.com/sites/yec/2018/10/02/be-one-get-one-the-importance-of-mentorship/#6dcda69c7434

8   Philippi, C. L., & Koenigs, M. (2014, July). The neuropsychology of self-reflection in psychiatric illness. Retrieved from https://www.ncbi.nlm.nih.gov/pmc/articles/PMC4022422/

FULL POTENTIAL

TOOLS FOR SUCCESS CONT.

9 Duckworth, A. (2019). Grit. London: Vermilion.

10 31 Benefits of Gratitude: The Ultimate Science-Backed Guide. (2020, February 28). Retrieved from https://www.happierhuman.com/benefits-of-gratitude/

TIPS FOR DIFFERENT LIFE STAGES

1 Linkedin by the Numbers: Stats, Demographics & Fun Facts. (2020, February 10). Retrieved March 8, 2020, from https://www.omnicoreagency.com/linkedin-statistics/

2 Fields, H. (2012, July 1). What is So Good About Growing Old. Retrieved July 1, 2019, from https://www.smithsonianmag.com/science-nature/what-is-so-good-about-growing-old-130839848/

3 Samuel, L. R. (2017, August 20). Are Older People Wiser? Retrieved March 8, 2020, from https://www.psychologytoday.com/us/blog/boomers-30/201708/are-older-people-wiser

GROWmyfuture.org

Please consider donating to GROW, a nonprofit founded by the author that helps youth identify their full potential. This work is especially important for youth who have few to no resources. GROW's goal is to instill confidence, agency, and competencies in students so they remain engaged in school, stay away from crime, and become thriving, contributing members of society. Change a teenager's life forever by helping them identify their value and job alignment.

ABOUT THE AUTHOR

Nicole Serena Silver has always had a knack for finding holes in systems. She looks at a situation, takes everything into consideration, and creates a whole approach to a solution. Her own struggles with finding her passion and calling motivated her to help others. She knew a solution was needed to address the biggest question we all face, "What do I want to do with my life?" It had to be a solution that was congruent with all the intricate parts of what makes us who we are, the lifestyle we want to create, and how our choices impact relationships in our lives.

For the past decade, Nicole has been submerged in research and development of curriculum that uncovers the intricate parts of who we are and how to pair our innate gifts with career and life choices. Nicole founded GROWmyfuture, which trains high school educators to deliver a curriculum that empowers youth to design their lives with tools that foster self discovery. After many years of adults asking if she had any resources available to help them discover their career and life path, she decided to write *Full Potential*.

Nicole is a multidisciplinary strategist, with an accomplished track record in roles involving trust-based relationships, leading entrepreneurial vision into implementation, and advancing individuals success with career goals. Nicole is a successful entrepreneur, business consultant, and educator. She has led workshops for fortune 500 companies, taught internationally and has been hired to advise numerous startups.